no-glamour sentence structure

Monica Gustafson

Skills:	Syntax, Grammar
Age Level:	5 thru 9
Grades:	K thru 4

LinguiSystems, Inc.
3100 4th Avenue
East Moline, IL 61244-9700
1-800 PRO IDEA
1-800-776-4332

FAX: 1-800-577-4555
E-mail: service@linguisystems.com
Web: www.linguisystems.com
TDD: 1-800-933-8331
(for those with hearing impairments)

Printed in the U.S.A.

ISBN 0-7606-0501-7

About the Author

Monica Gustafson has been a speech language pathologist in the St. James-Assiniboia School Division in Winnipeg, Manitoba, Canada since 1977. Monica is responsible for intervention to elementary-aged students and providing storytelling to children throughout the division. She also writes a column for the Winnipeg Parent Newsmagazine to promote public awareness of speech and language. An author of numerous speech and language programs, this is Monica's first publication with LinguiSystems.

Monica and her husband Ron live in Winnipeg with their two children, Kari and Erik. In her spare time Monica enjoys reading, traveling, and volunteering as a recruitment advisor for her chapter of Kappa Alpha Theta.

Dedication

"Some people come into our lives and quickly go. Some stay for a while and leave footprints on our hearts that last a lifetime."

Anonymous

This book is dedicated to my American "mom and dad," Irene and Larry Rutherford, who welcomed me into their family during my college years and truly made me feel like their "Canadian daughter."

Cover Design by Chris Claus
Page Layout by Jamie Bellagamba
Illustrations by Margaret Warner
Edited by Barb Truman

Table of Contents

Introduction

No-Glamour Sentence Structure is a flexible, picture-based program to help students develop more complicated sentence structures. The worksheets are arranged in order of complexity from simple sentences to more complex structures and negative forms. In no way is it suggested that this is a hierarchy of the way students develop these structures. The order was established to help students increase the complexity of their structures from simple to more complex.

Each unit begins with a suggested list of sentences, followed by the individual worksheets. On each worksheet page, the complexity of the sentence is developed by the illustrations, step-by-step, until the student has verbally described each element. Once all the elements of the sentence have been identified, the student can then construct a complete sentence structure.

When working with a student, use a meta-cognitive modeling method to suggest appropriate structures as in the example below. An example of modeling is provided on the first page of each unit.

Example (page 186):
"The first picture shows us '**The boy**.' Let's write that under the picture. In the next picture, what has changed? He is on a swing. We might say '**on the swing**.' Let's write that down. Now what is the boy doing in the next picture? '**Smiling**.' Let's add '**is smiling**' under that picture. Now let's put it all together to tell everything that is happening in the last picture. '**The boy on the swing is smiling**.' "

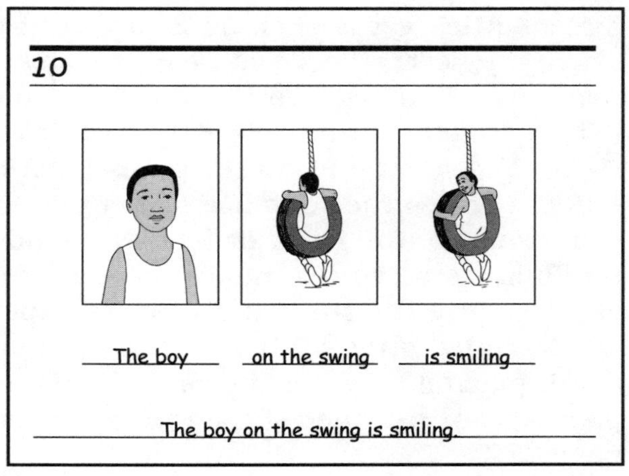

For most of the stimulus pages, the suggested text is written in the present tense, but you can change the text to meet the goals of individual students.

Example (page 8):
The boy is running.
The boy runs.
The boy ran.
The boy will run.

The suggested text is also written with nouns. You can change these nouns to target the use of pronouns as needed.

Examples:
(page 38) The little girl is reading. → She is reading.

(page 62) The children are jumping rope. → They are jumping rope.

Introduction

Although there are suggested adjectives and adverbs with some sentences, encourage students to choose their own descriptors and/or add other adjectives or adverbs that might not even be illustrated.

Example (page 14):
The girl is skiing.
The little girl with the hat and scarf is skiing downhill.

Students with language disorders are typically not efficient auditory learners, so in working with this population, it is appropriate that we provide them with as many visual cues as possible. This program was designed with these children in mind. The program gives them a visual strategy to build sentence structures and to practice both formulating those structures and writing them coherently.

Some students may have difficulty remembering all the words in sentences. For example, they may forget "little" words such as *is*, *are*, and *who*. There are several ways you can help by providing more visual cueing. You might draw an oval link between picture frames like the example on the right. You can fill in these spaces before the student writes the sentence to remind him of the occurrence of the form, or have the student fill in the links as he writes the completed structure. You can also give the student a piece of paper with the word printed on it so that he can manipulate the word, placing it in the appropriate spot on the page. We've provided these words for your use on page 272.

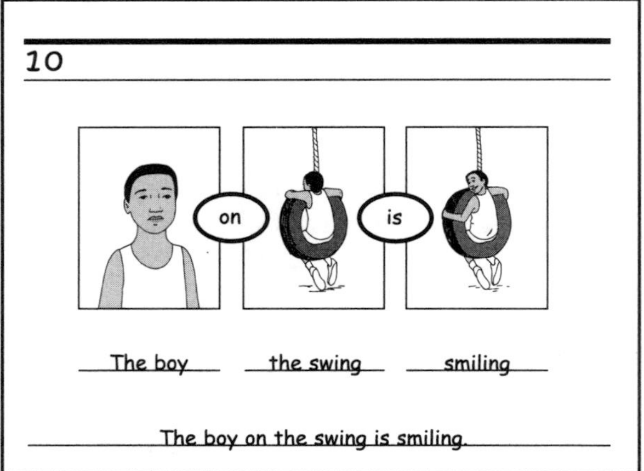

Other visual strategies are to highlight the word, write it in a different color, or draw a shape around the word. You could choose different shapes for different words to help cue the student visually. For example, you might draw a circle around every *is*, a square around every *who*, and a triangle around every *the*.

My students have demonstrated a better understanding of sentence structures using this program and have gone on to use them in less structured situations. I wish you success in building your students' use of appropriate sentence structures with the strategies suggested in *No-Glamour Sentence Structure*.

Monica

Noun + Verb

1. The boy is running.
2. The boy is swimming.
3. The boy is swinging.
4. The boy is reading.
5. The girl is skipping.
6. The girl is sewing.
7. The girl is skiing.
8. The girl is singing.
9. The girl is smiling.
10. The baby is crawling.
11. The children are coloring.
12. The children are playing.
13. The children are skating.
14. The children are painting.
15. The cat is scratching.
16. The dog is digging.
17. The bird is singing.
18. The owl is flying.
19. The parrot is talking.
20. The snowman is melting.

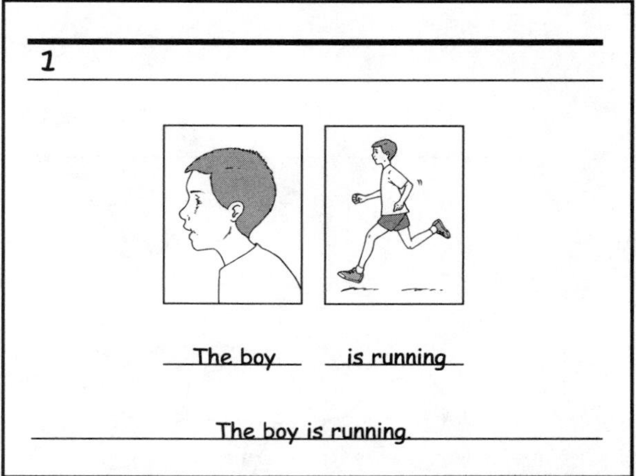

Modeling Example:

1. The first picture shows "**The boy**." Let's write that under the picture.
2. In the next picture, what has changed? The boy is running. We might say "**is running**." Let's write "**is running**" under that picture.
3. Now let's put the words all together to tell everything that is happening in the last picture. "**The boy is running**."

1

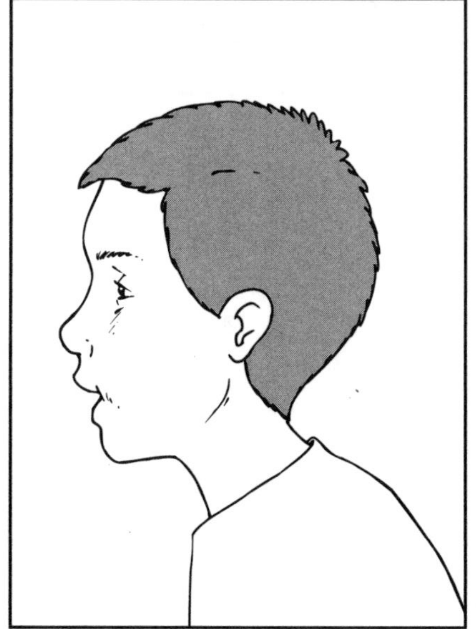

2

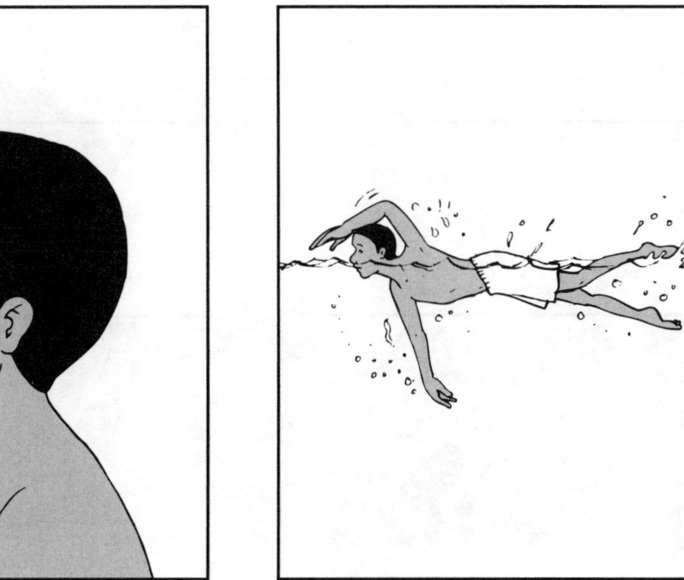

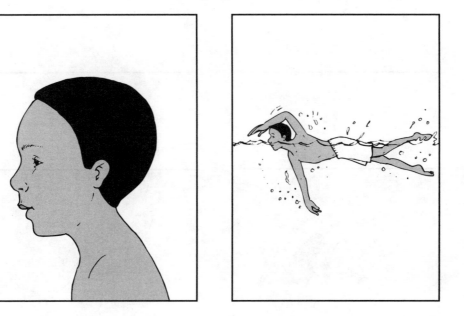

3

4

5

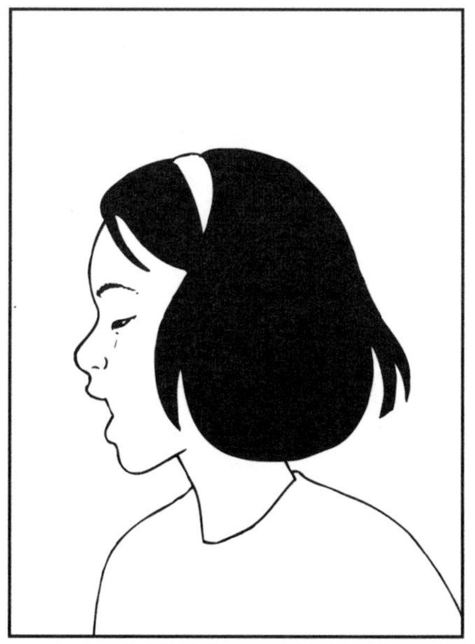

6

7

8

9

10

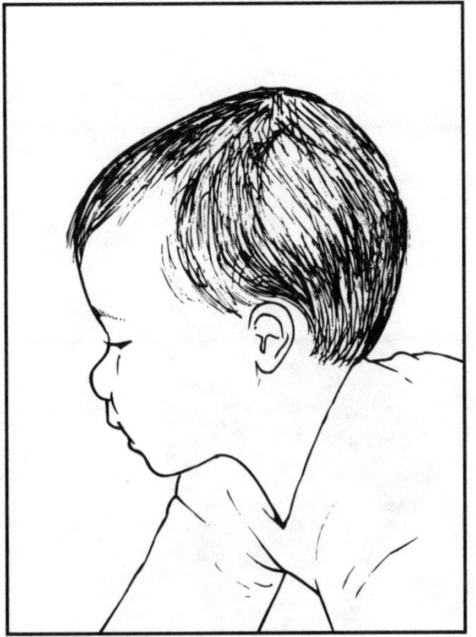

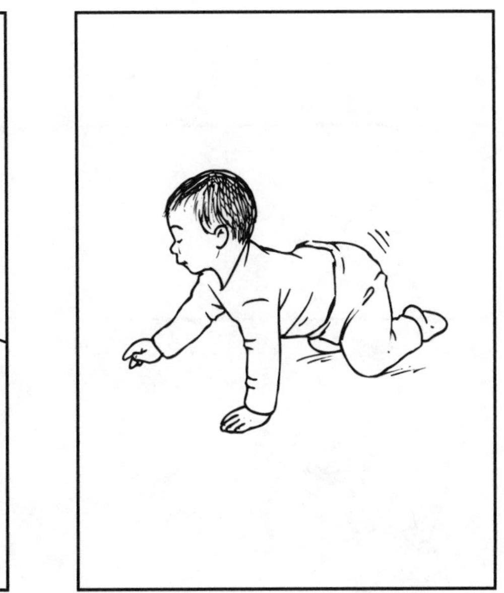

11

12

13

14

15

16

18

19

20

Adjective + Noun + Verb

1. The tall boy is jumping.
2. The fluffy cat is eating.
3. The long dog is digging.
4. The happy boy is swinging.
5. The small dog is barking.
6. The striped cat is sleeping.
7. The sad girl is crying.
8. The big bear is climbing.
9. The large lion is roaring.
10. The little girl is reading.
11. The shaggy dog is scratching.
12. The polar bear is swimming.
13. The tiny baby is sleeping.
14. The dirty boy is washing.
15. The tired man is resting.
16. The first child is laughing.
17. The spotted dog is sleeping.
18. The last man is drinking.
19. The cracked glass is leaking.
20. The sleepy boy is yawning.

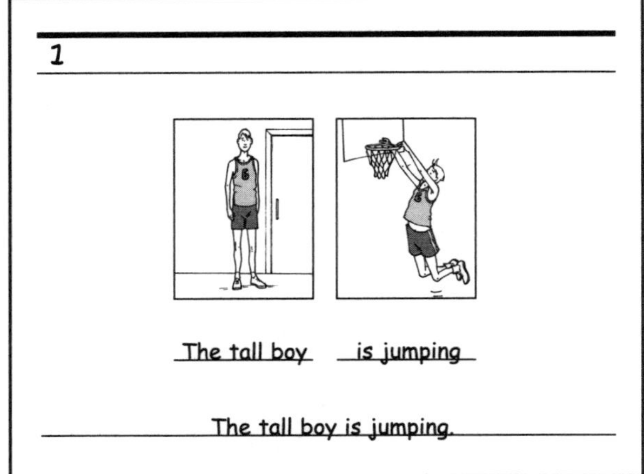

Modeling Example:

1. The first picture shows a boy. What can you say about the boy? He is tall. We might say "**The tall boy**." Let's write that under the picture.
2. In the next picture, what has changed? The boy is jumping. Let's write "**is jumping**" under that picture.
3. Now let's put the words all together to tell everything that is happening in the last picture. "**The tall boy is jumping**."

1

2

3

4

5

6

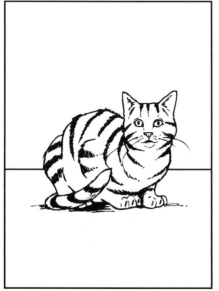

7

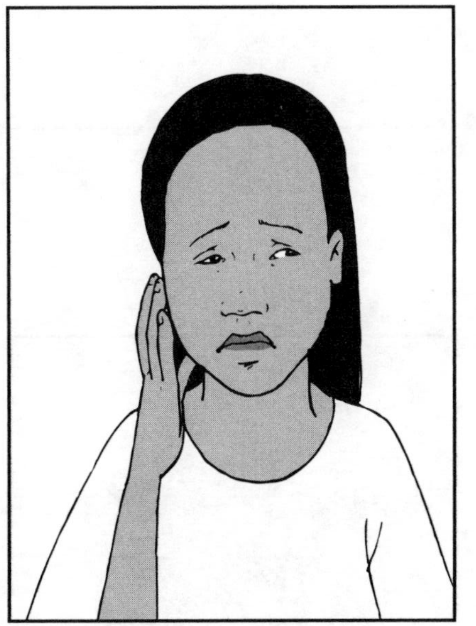

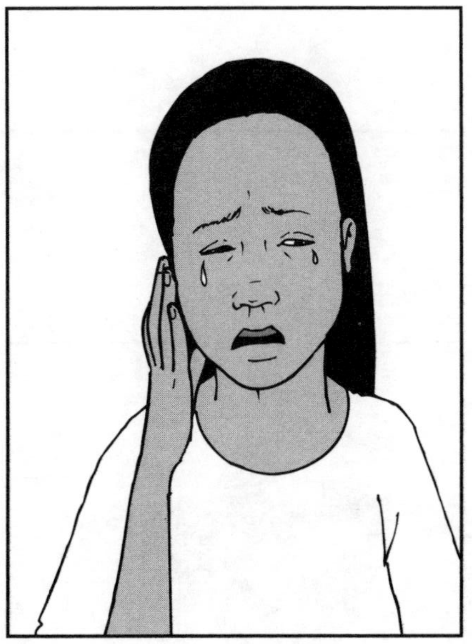

8

9

10

11

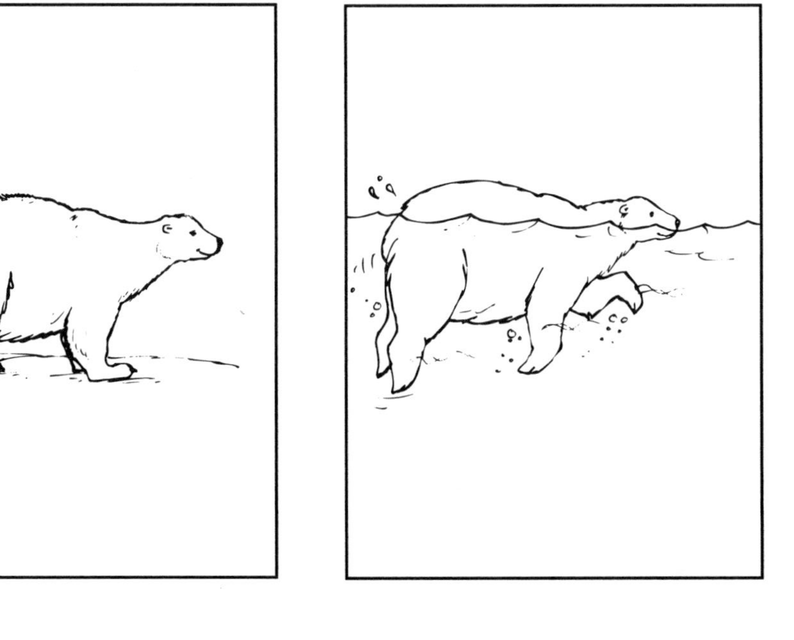

13

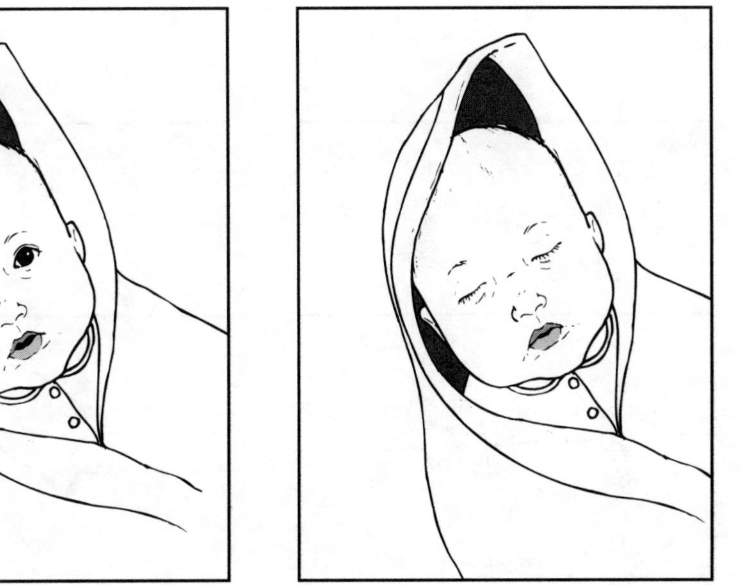

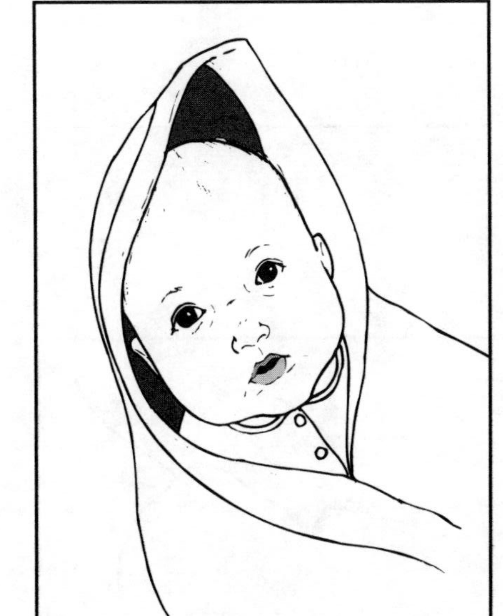

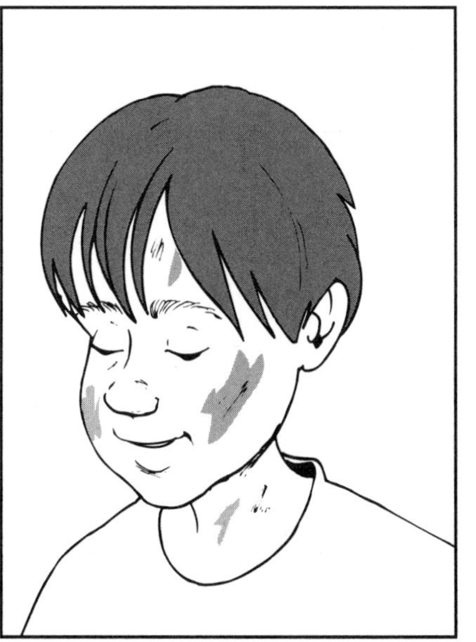

15

16

17

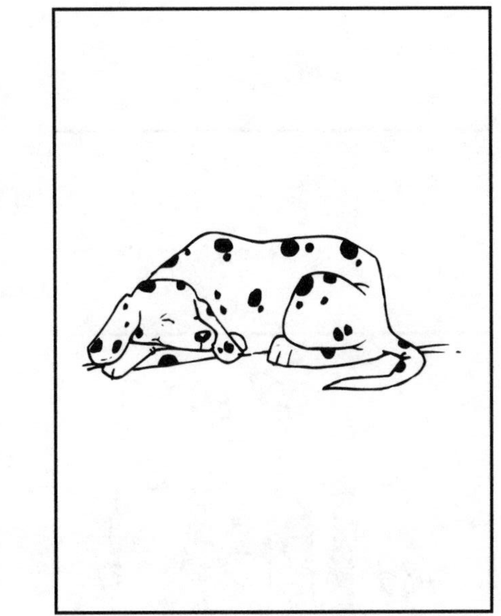

18

19

20

Noun + Verb + Direct Object

1. The boy is reading a newspaper.
2. The boy is painting a picture.
3. The boy is eating an apple.
4. The boy is cutting paper.
5. The boy is drinking soda.
6. The girl is petting a dog.
7. The girl is licking ice cream.
8. The girl is riding a bike.
9. The girl is wrapping a present.
10. The girl is pulling a wagon.
11. The girl is washing her face.
12. The children are building a castle.
13. The children are jumping rope.
14. The children are building a snowman.
15. The children are washing a dog.
16. The dog is eating a bone.
17. The dog is chasing the cat.
18. The cat is licking her paw.
19. The bird is building a nest.
20. The goat is chewing the laundry.

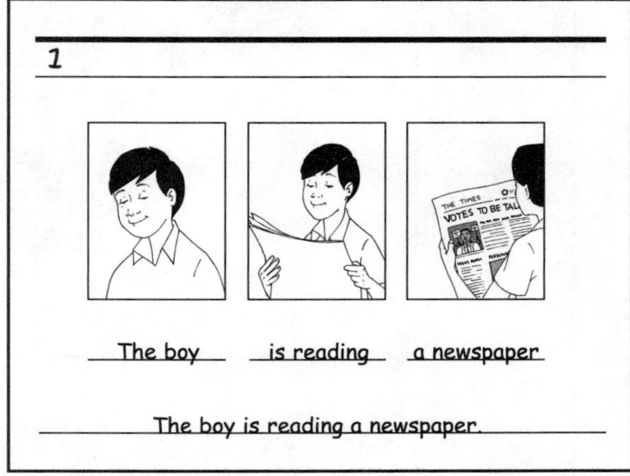
1
THE TIMES
VOTES TO BE TAL
The boy
is reading
a newspaper
The boy is reading a newspaper.

Modeling Example:

1. The first picture shows "**The boy**." Let's write that under the picture.
2. In the next picture, what has changed? The boy is reading. We might say "**is reading**." Let's write that down.
3. Look at the next picture. What is the boy reading? "**A newspaper**." Let's write that under the picture.
4. Now let's put the words all together to tell everything that is happening in the last picture. "**The boy is reading a newspaper**."

1

2

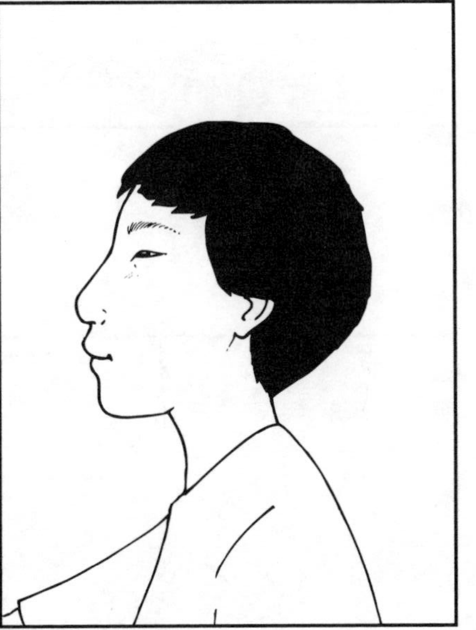

3

4

5

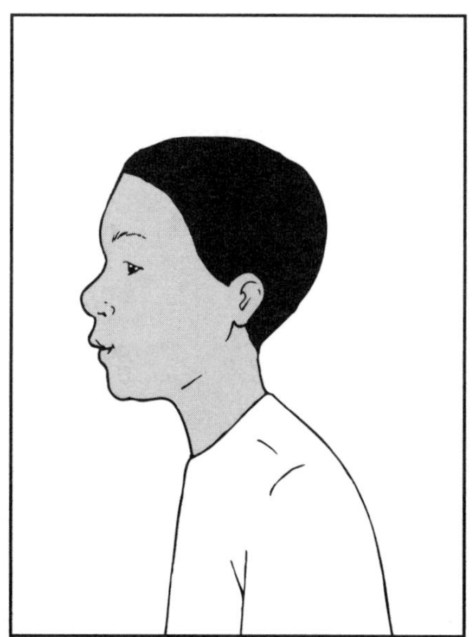

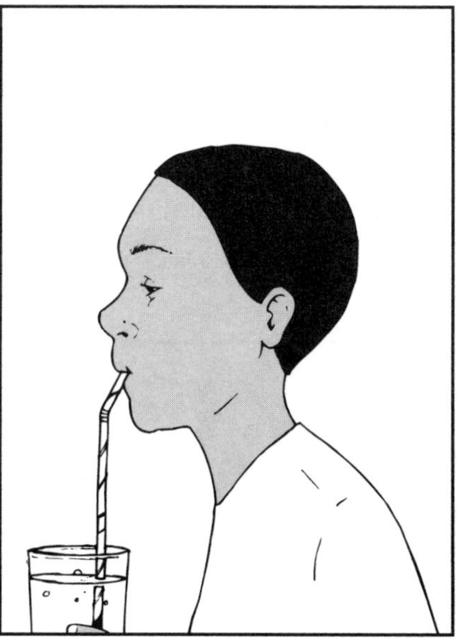

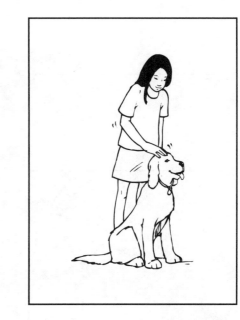

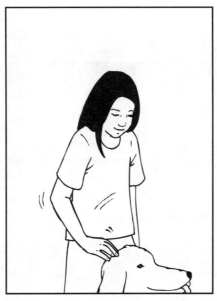

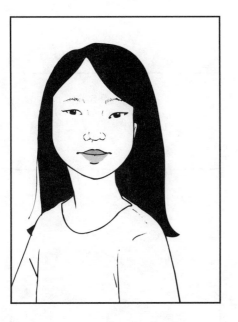

7

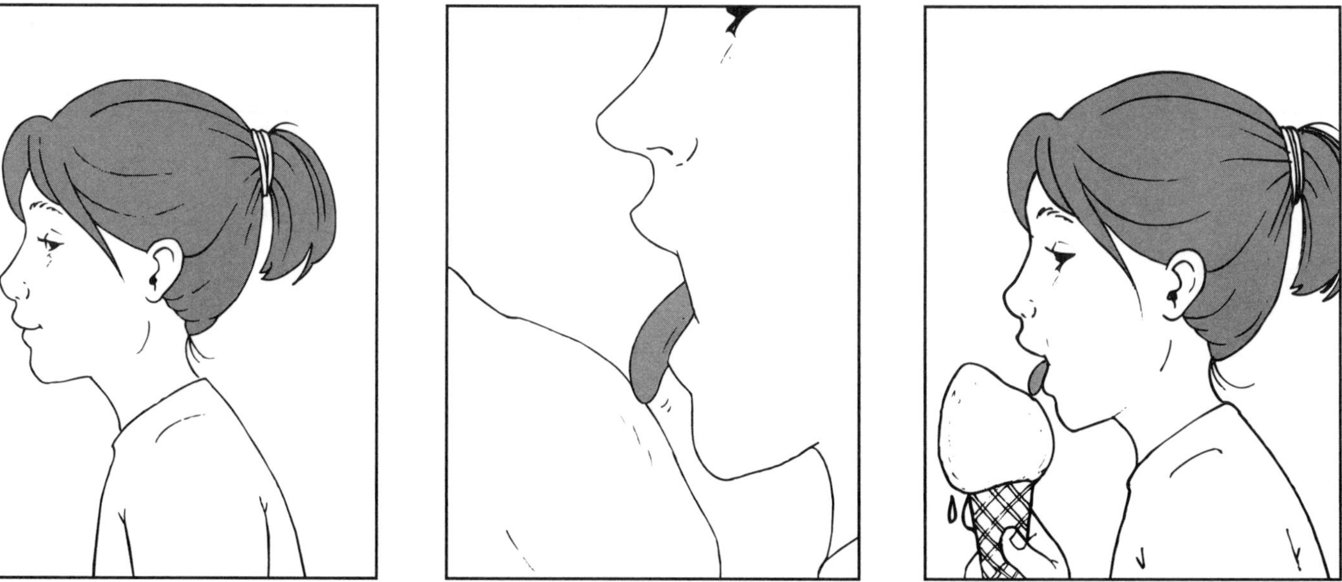

8

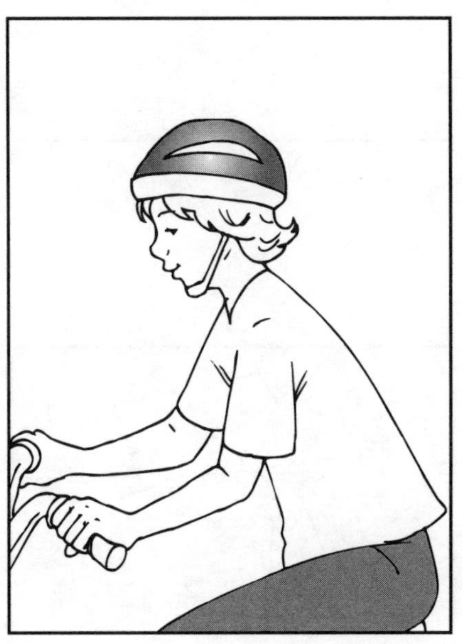

9

10

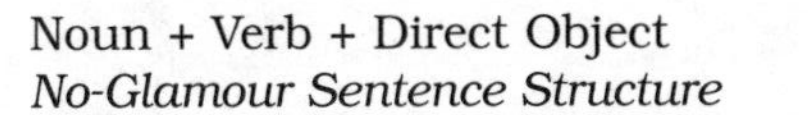

11

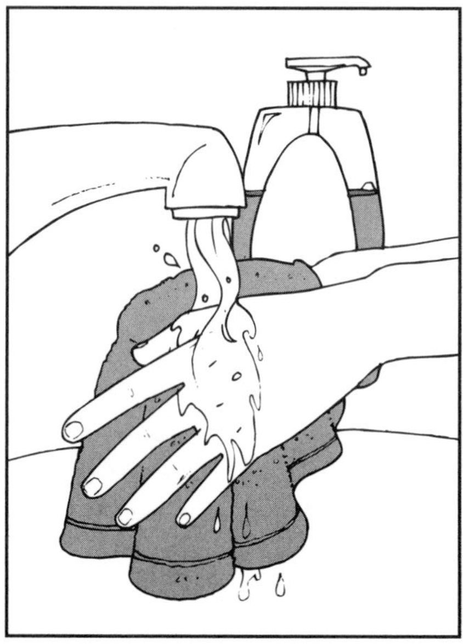

12

13

14

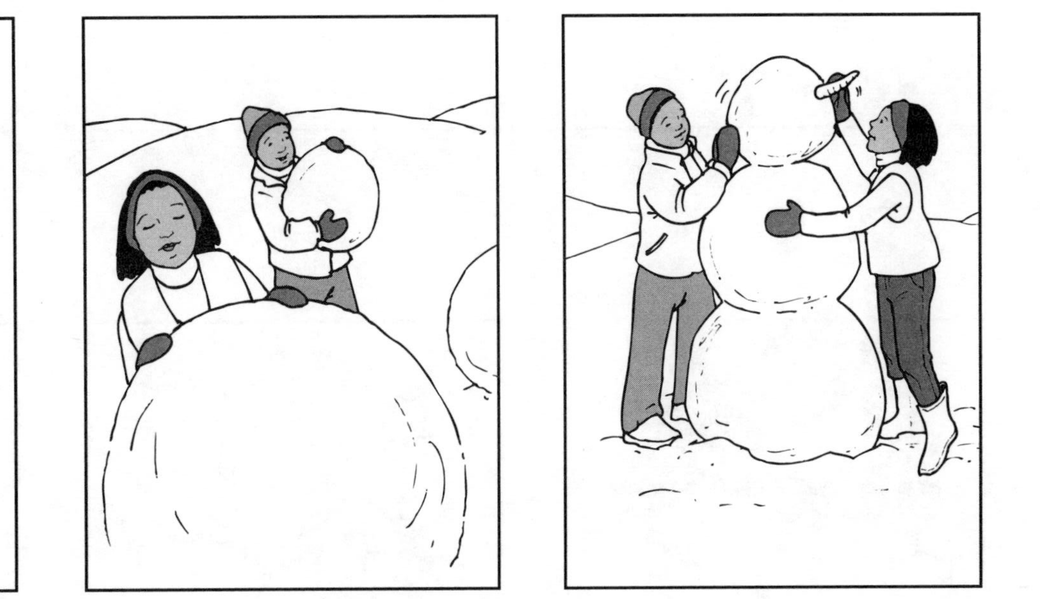

______________________ ______________________ ______________________

Noun + Verb + Direct Object
No-Glamour Sentence Structure

15

16

17

18

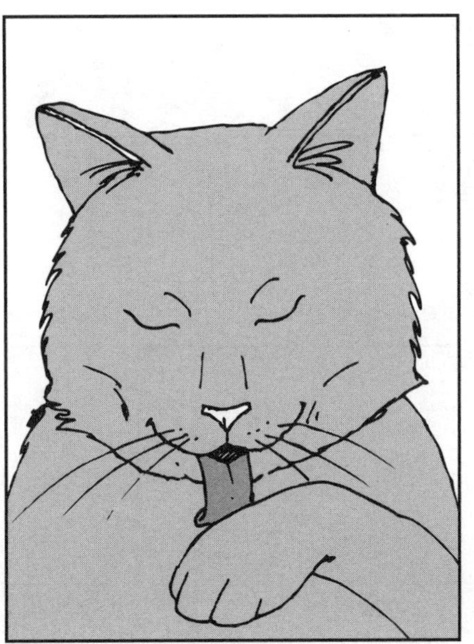

19

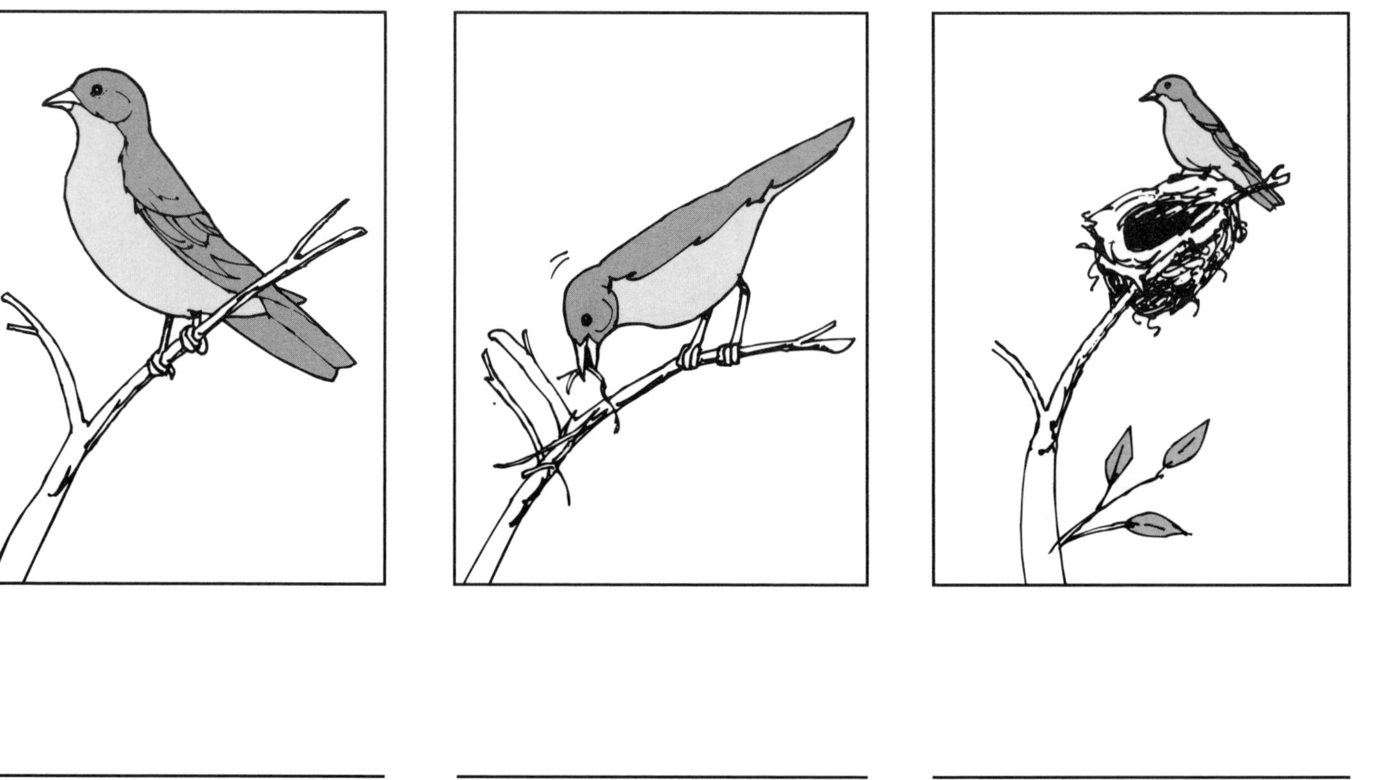

20

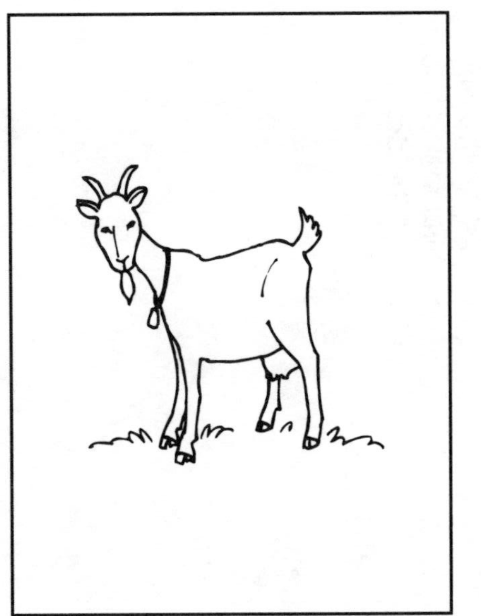

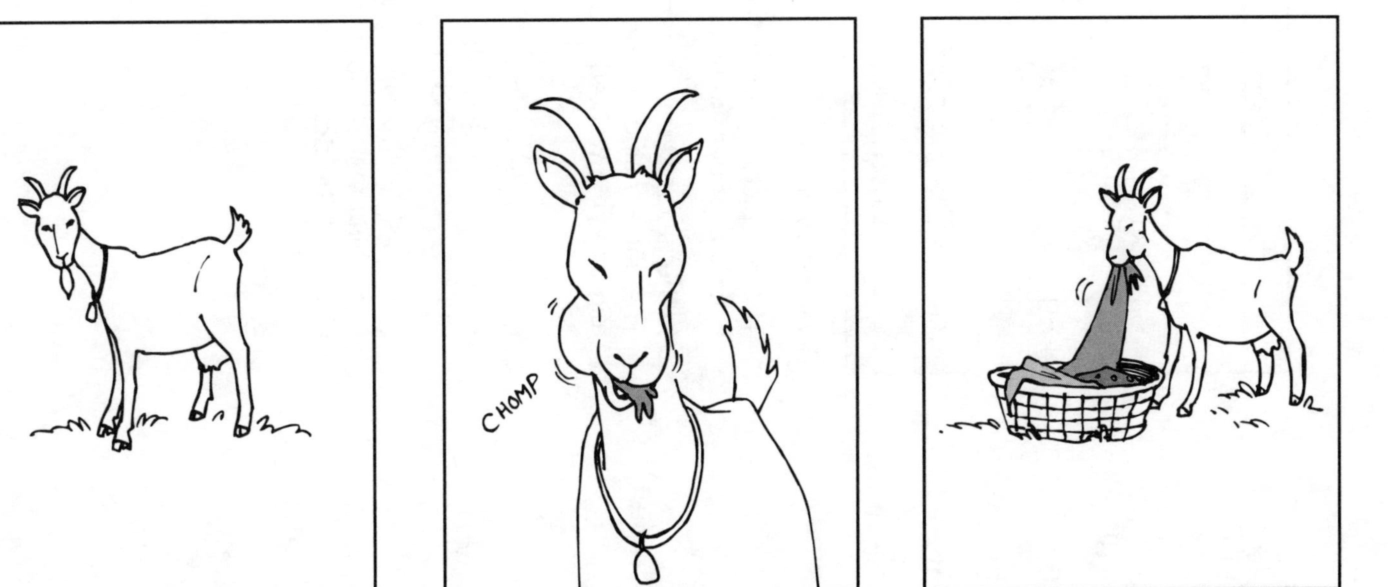

Noun + Passive Verb + Prepositional Phrase

1. The dog is walked by the boy.
2. The baby is dressed by the mother.
3. The birds are fed by the boy.
4. The picture was drawn by the girl.
5. The sweater was knitted by the woman.
6. The chair was scratched by the cat.
7. The shoe was found by the boy.
8. The newspaper was read by the man.
9. The horse is ridden by the cowboy.
10. The glass was broken by the girl.
11. The apple was eaten by the boy.
12. The window was broken by the ball.
13. The girl was sprayed by the elephant.
14. The boat is rowed by the boy.
15. The telephone was answered by the boy.
16. The dog is chased by the squirrel.
17. The balloon was popped by the clown.
18. The candles were blown out by the girl.
19. The fire was sprayed by the firefighter.
20. The ball was hit by the girl.

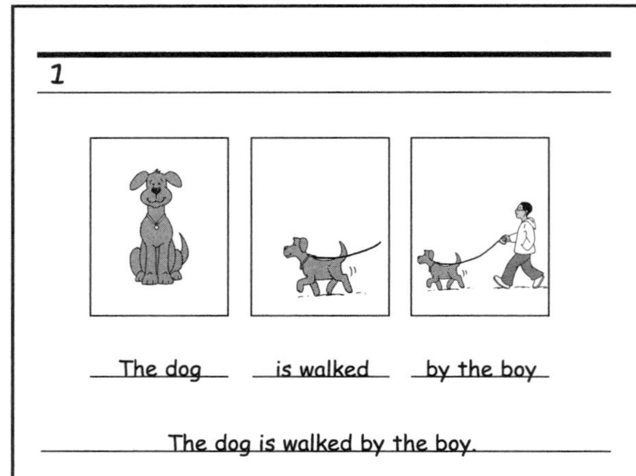

Modeling Example:

1. The first picture shows "**The dog**." Let's write that under the picture.
2. In the next picture, what has changed? The dog is being walked by someone. We might say "**is walked**." Let's write that down.
3. Look at the next picture. Who is the dog walked by? By the boy. Let's write "**by the boy**" under that picture.
4. Now let's put the words all together to tell everything that is happening in the last picture. "**The dog is walked by the boy**."

1

2

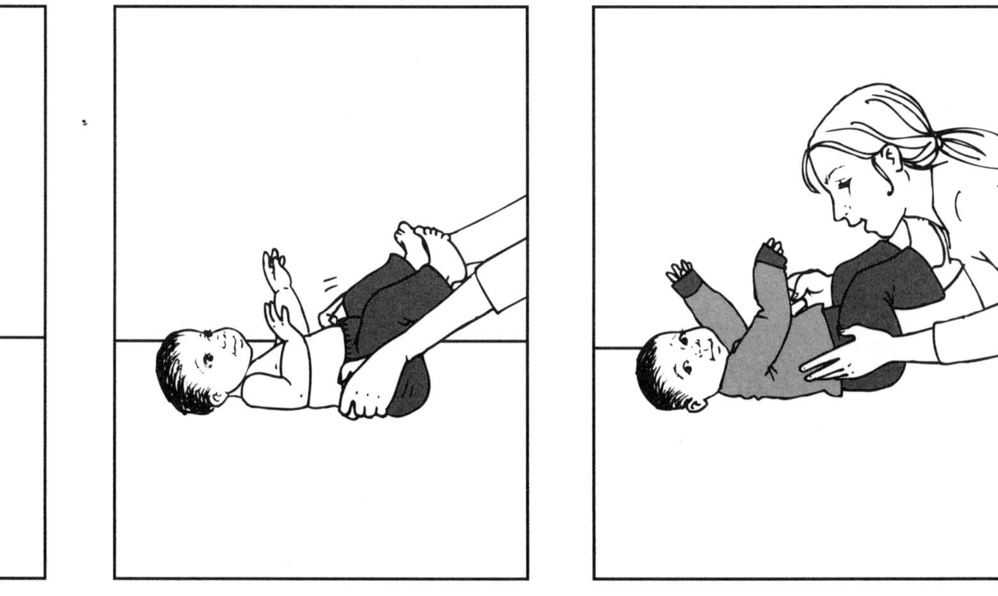

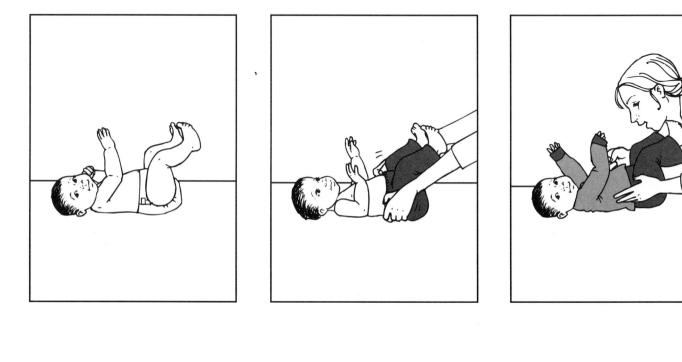

3

______________________ ______________________ ______________________

Nind

Nind

5

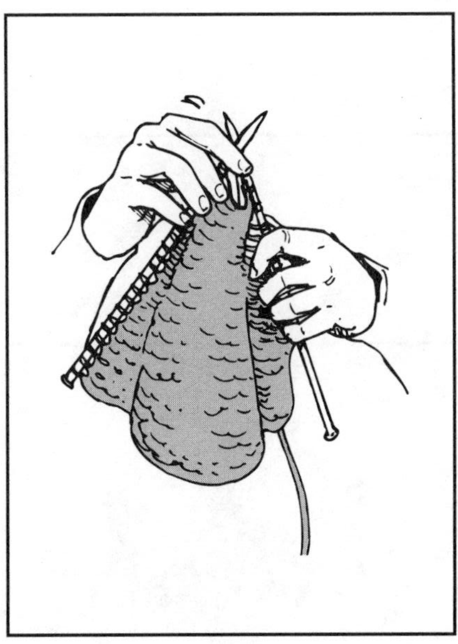

6

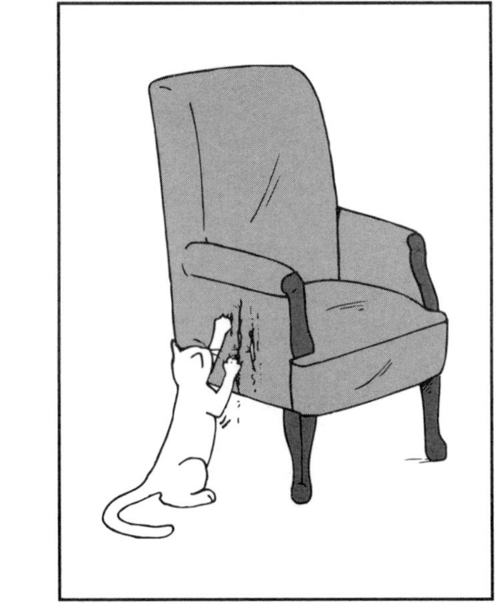

7

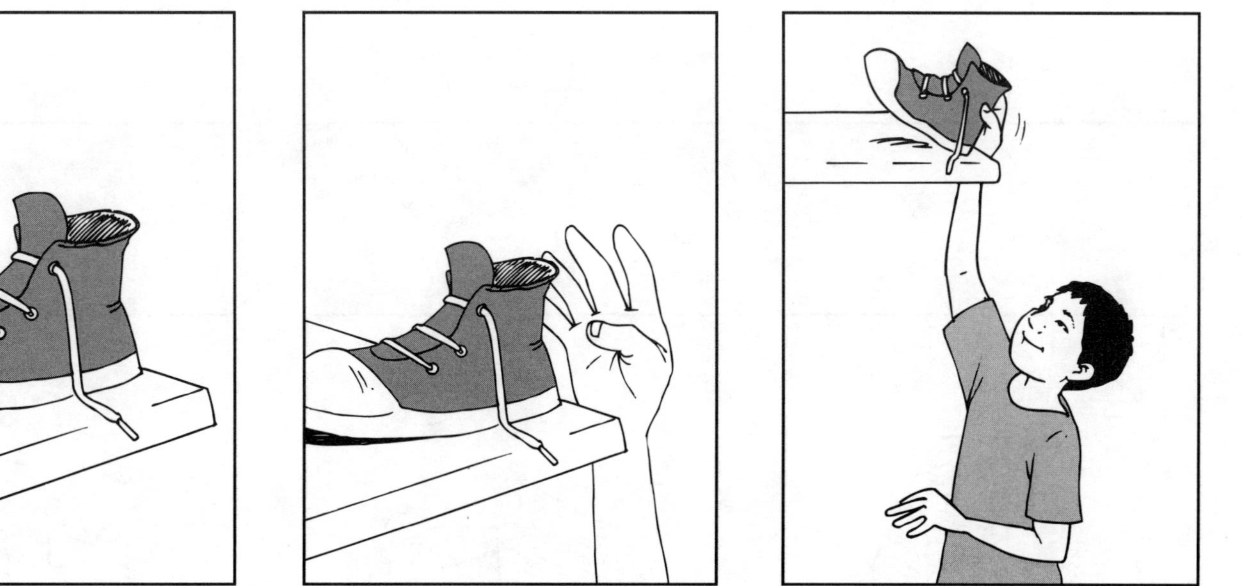

8

9

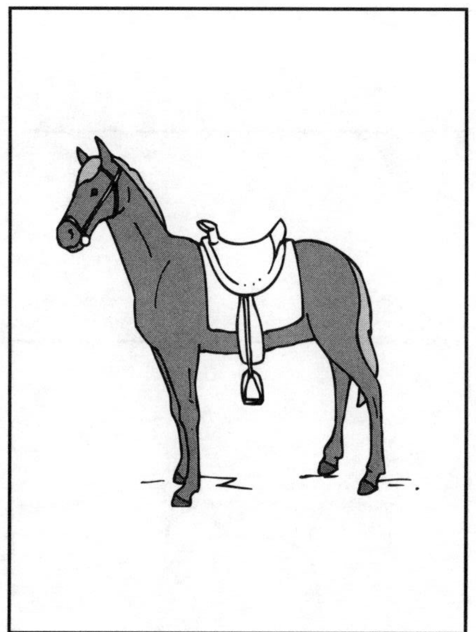

10

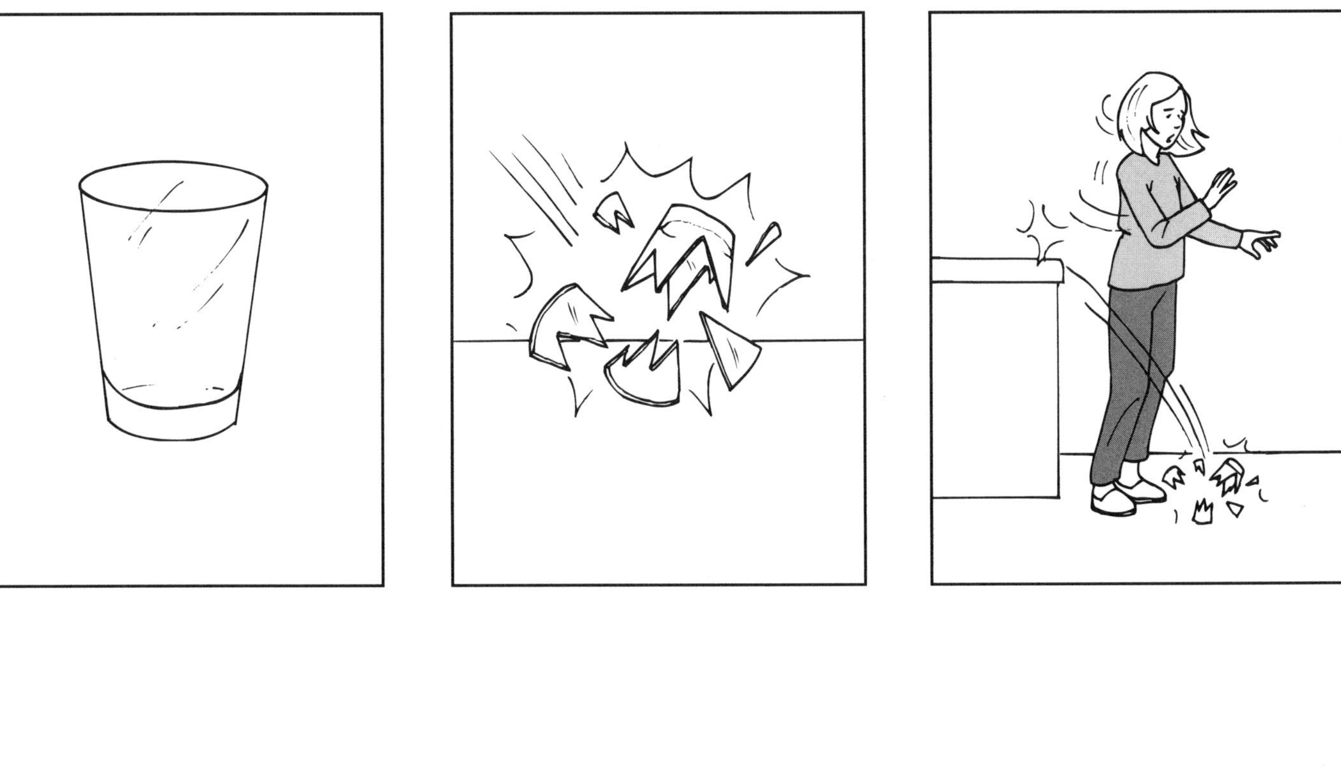

11

12

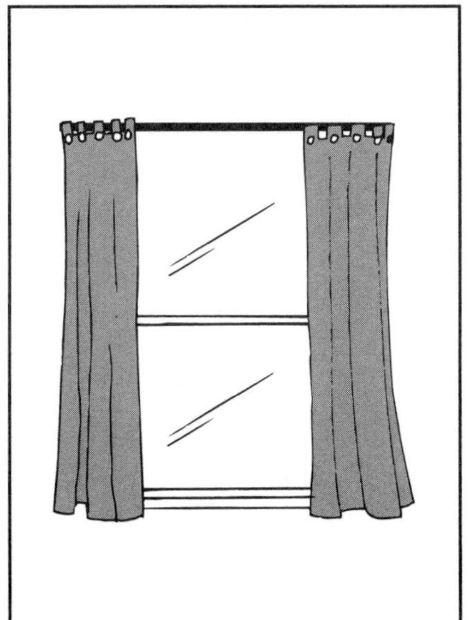

13

14

15

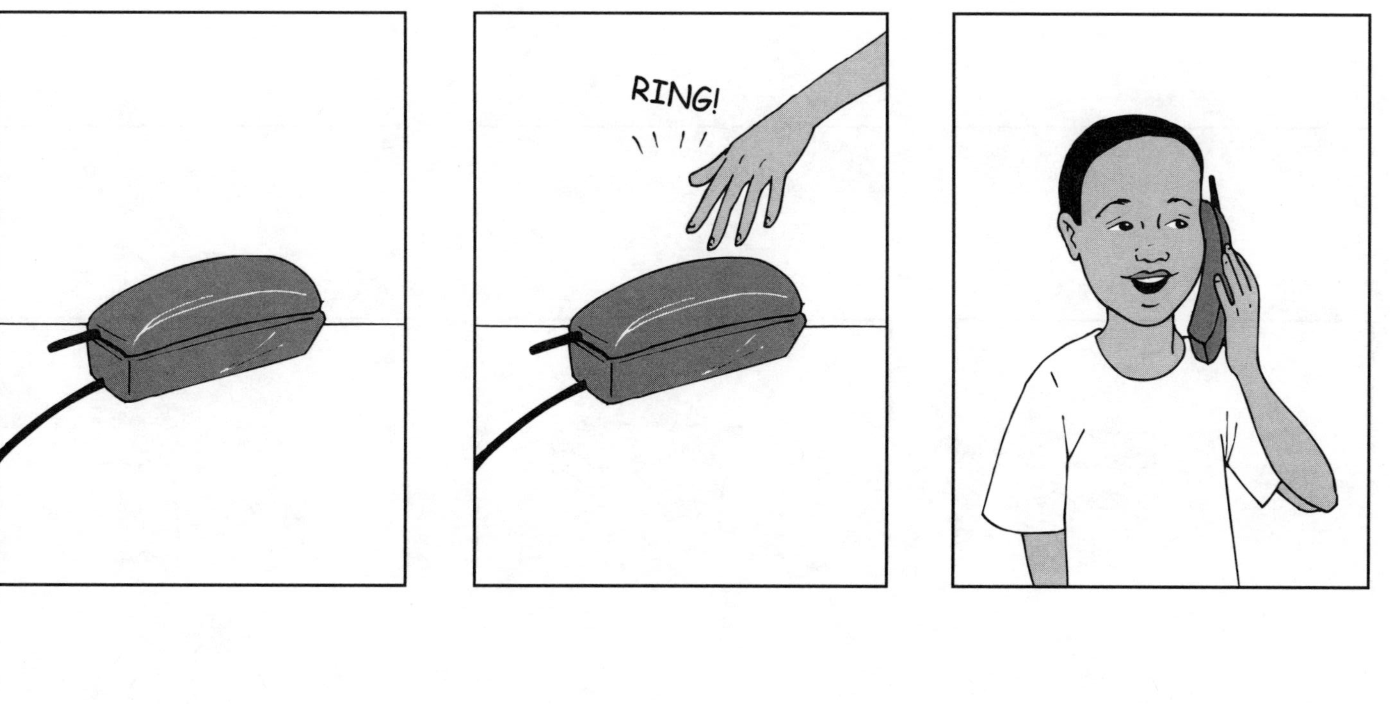

16

17

18

19

20

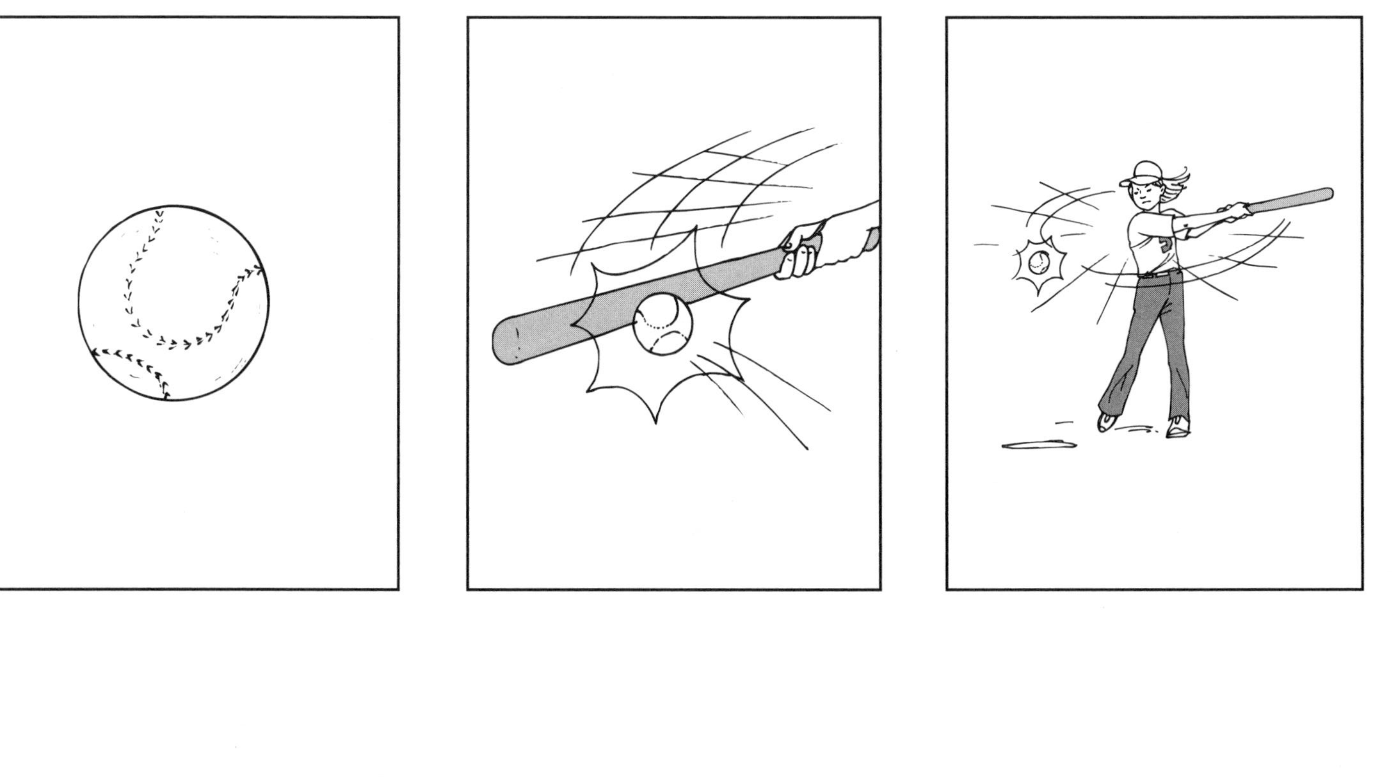

Noun + Verb + Indirect Object + Object

1. The boy is giving the dog a bone.
2. The mother is giving the child medicine.
3. The man is buying the woman flowers.
4. The clown is giving the child a balloon.
5. The mom is throwing the boy a ball.
6. The mom is cutting the child a piece.
7. The girl is picking the boy an apple.
8. The woman is sewing the girl a dress.
9. The woman is knitting the baby a sweater.
10. The woman is making the children popcorn.

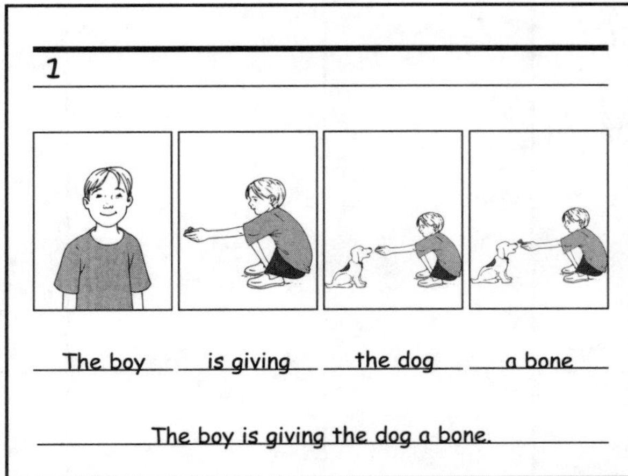

Modeling Example:

1. The first picture shows "**The boy**." Let's write that under the picture.
2. In the next picture, what has changed? The boy is giving something. We might say "**is giving**." Let's write that down.
3. Look at the next picture. Who is the boy giving something to? "**The dog**." Let's write that under that picture.
4. Look at the next picture. What is the boy giving to the dog? "**A bone**." Let's write that under the picture.
5. Now let's put the words all together to tell everything that is happening in the last picture. "**The boy is giving the dog a bone**."

1

2

3

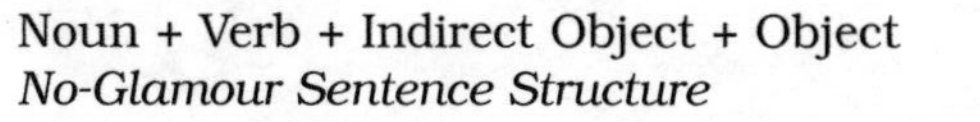

5

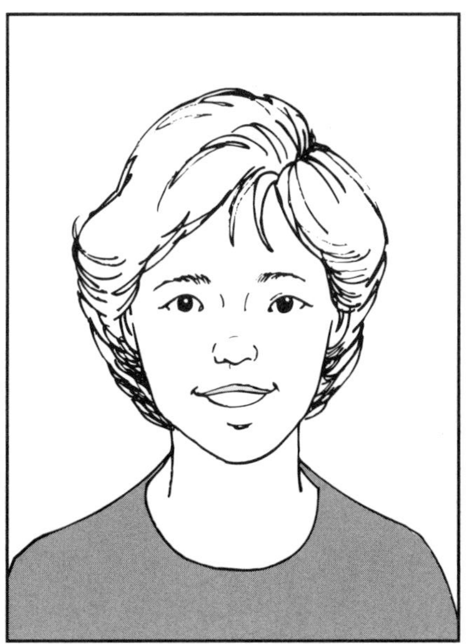

6

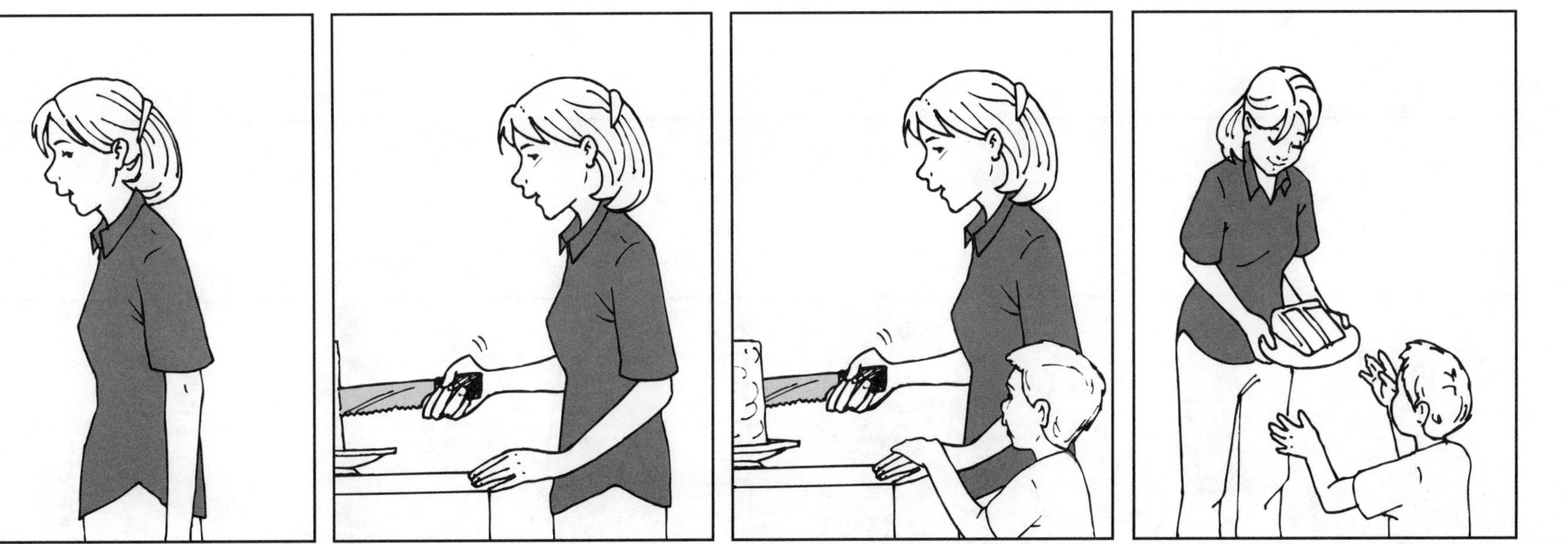

7

8

9

10

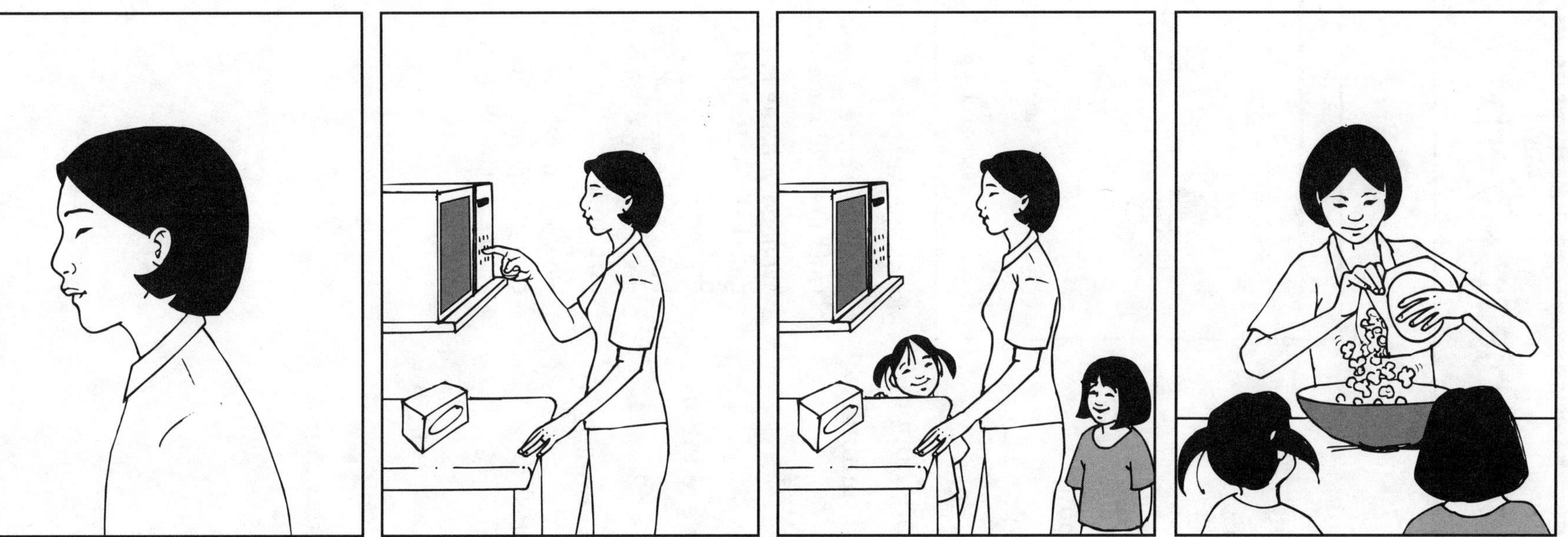

Compound Subject + Verb

1. The boy and the girl are smiling.
2. The boy and the girl are swinging.
3. The boy and the girl are waving.
4. The girl and the boy are hiding.
5. The girl and the dog are drinking.
6. The boy and the cat are sleeping.
7. The girl and the cat are stretching.
8. The dog and the cat are fighting.
9. The kangaroo and the rabbit are hopping.
10. The fish and the turtle are swimming.
11. The birds and the bees are flying.
12. The bee and the fly are buzzing.
13. The grandmother and the boy are talking.
14. The teacher and the boy are smiling.
15. The mother and the girl are shopping.
16. The father and the girl are reading.
17. The father and the boy are playing.
18. The grandfather and the boy are hugging.
19. The cat and the dog are scratching.
20. The moon and the stars are shining.

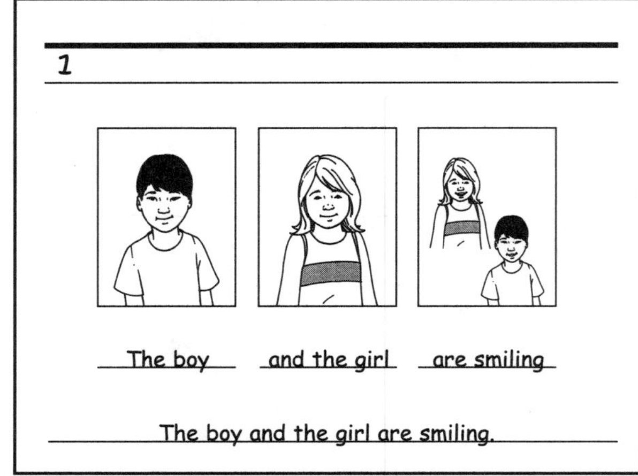
1
The boy
and the girl
are smiling
The boy and the girl are smiling.

Modeling Example:

1. The first picture shows "**The boy**." Let's write that under the picture.
2. What do you see in the next picture? The girl. Let's write "**and the girl**" under the picture.
3. Look at the last picture. What are the boy and girl doing? Smiling. We might say "**are smiling**." Let's write that down.
4. Now let's put the words all together to tell everything that is happening in the last picture. "**The boy and the girl are smiling**."

1

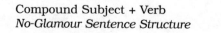

2

3

4

5

6

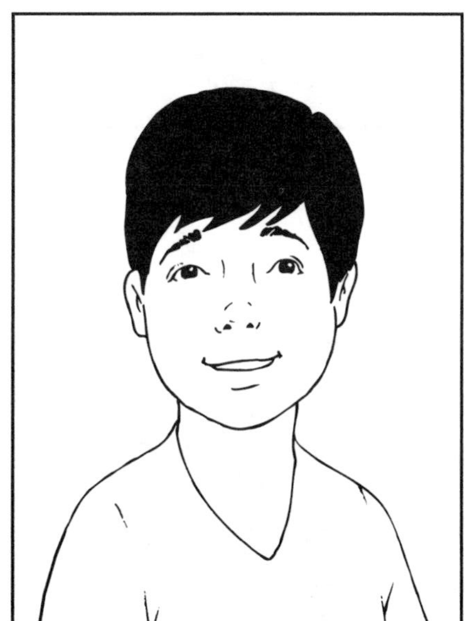

7

8

9

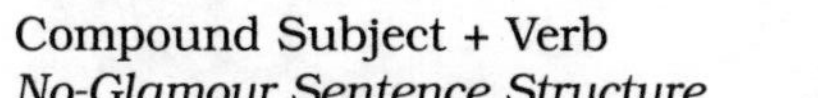

10

11

12

13

14

15

16

17

18

19

20

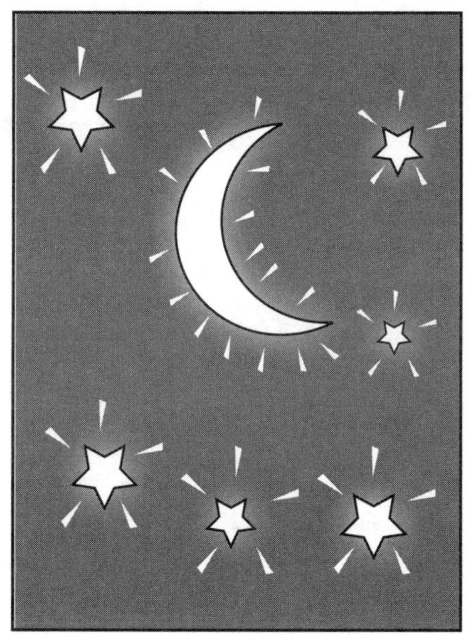

Noun + Compound Verb

1. The girl is singing and dancing.
2. The girl is sliding and waving.
3. The girl is walking and eating.
4. The girls are smiling and hugging.
5. The girls are drawing and coloring.
6. The girl is stretching and yawning.
7. The boy is running and drinking.
8. The boy is eating and drinking.
9. The boy is digging and sweating.
10. The children are watching and waiting.
11. The children are riding and pointing.
12. The children are throwing and catching.
13. The children are cutting and folding.
14. The man is walking and talking.
15. The man is sleeping and snoring.
16. The man is writing and drinking.
17. The man is lifting and stacking.
18. The woman is watching and crying.
19. The woman is driving and pointing.
20. The dog is jumping and catching.

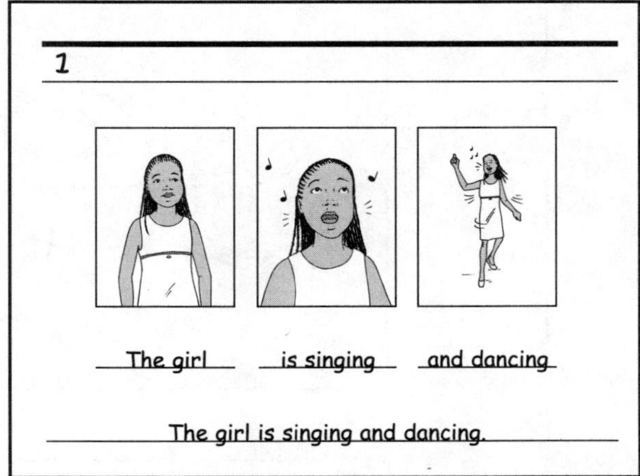

Modeling Example:

1. The first picture shows "**The girl**." Let's write that under the picture.
2. In the next picture, what has changed? The girl is singing. We might say "**is singing**." Let's write that down.
3. Look at the next picture. Now what is the girl doing? Dancing. Let's write "**and dancing**" under that picture.
4. Now let's put the words all together to tell everything that is happening in the last picture. "**The girl is singing and dancing**."

1

2

3

5

6

7

8

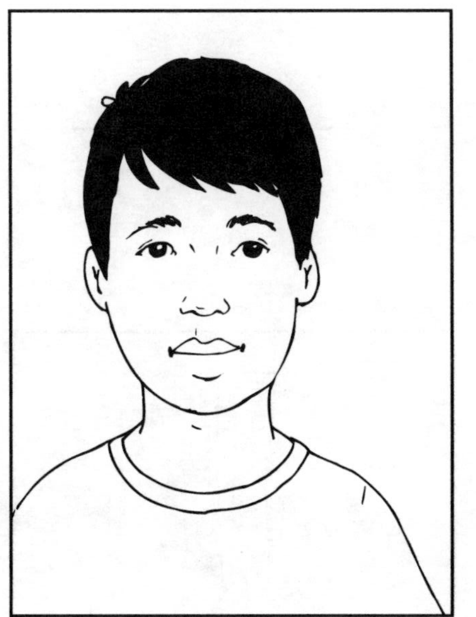

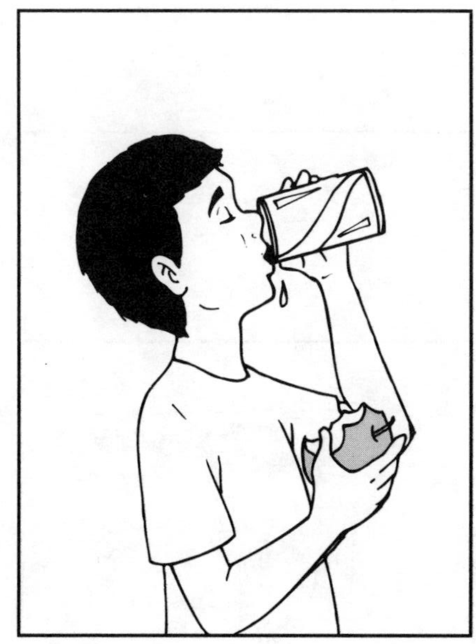

9

10

11

12

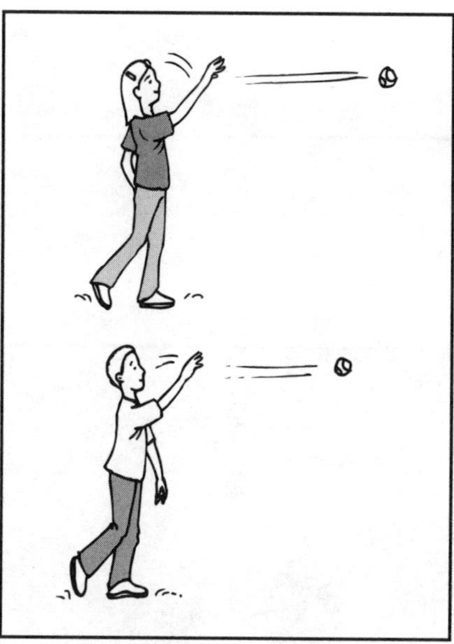

13

14

15

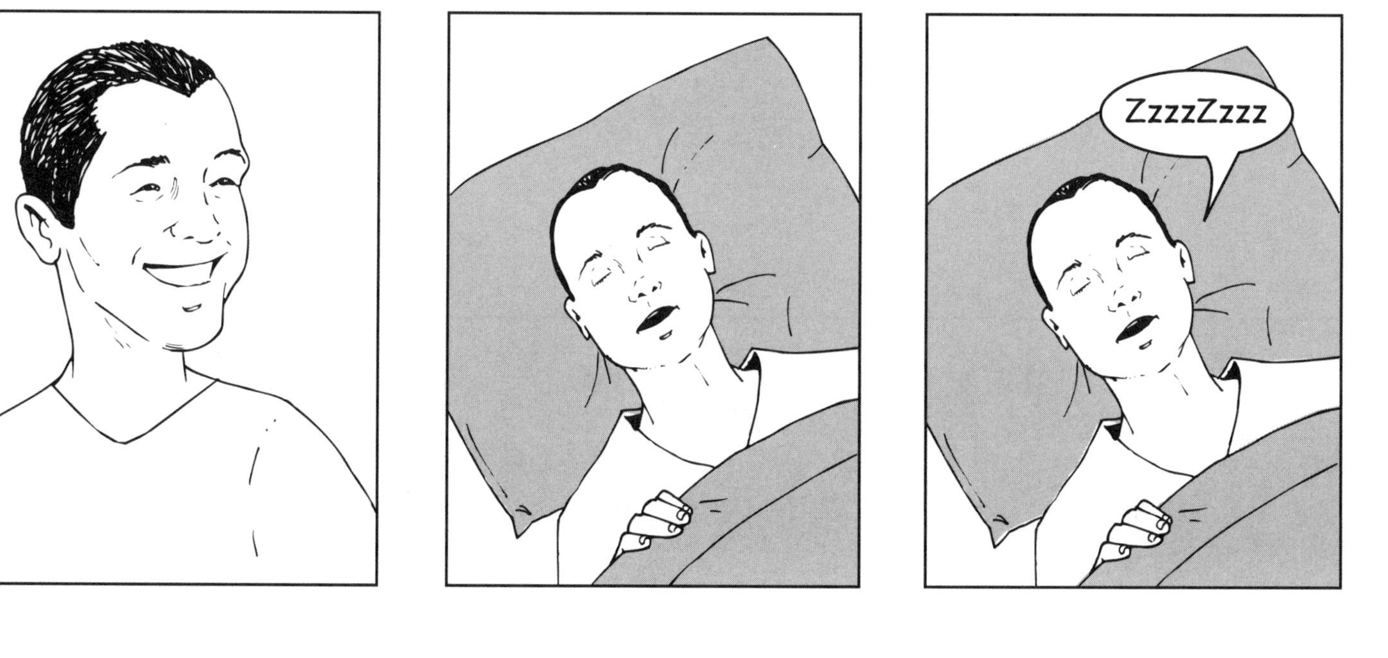

16

17

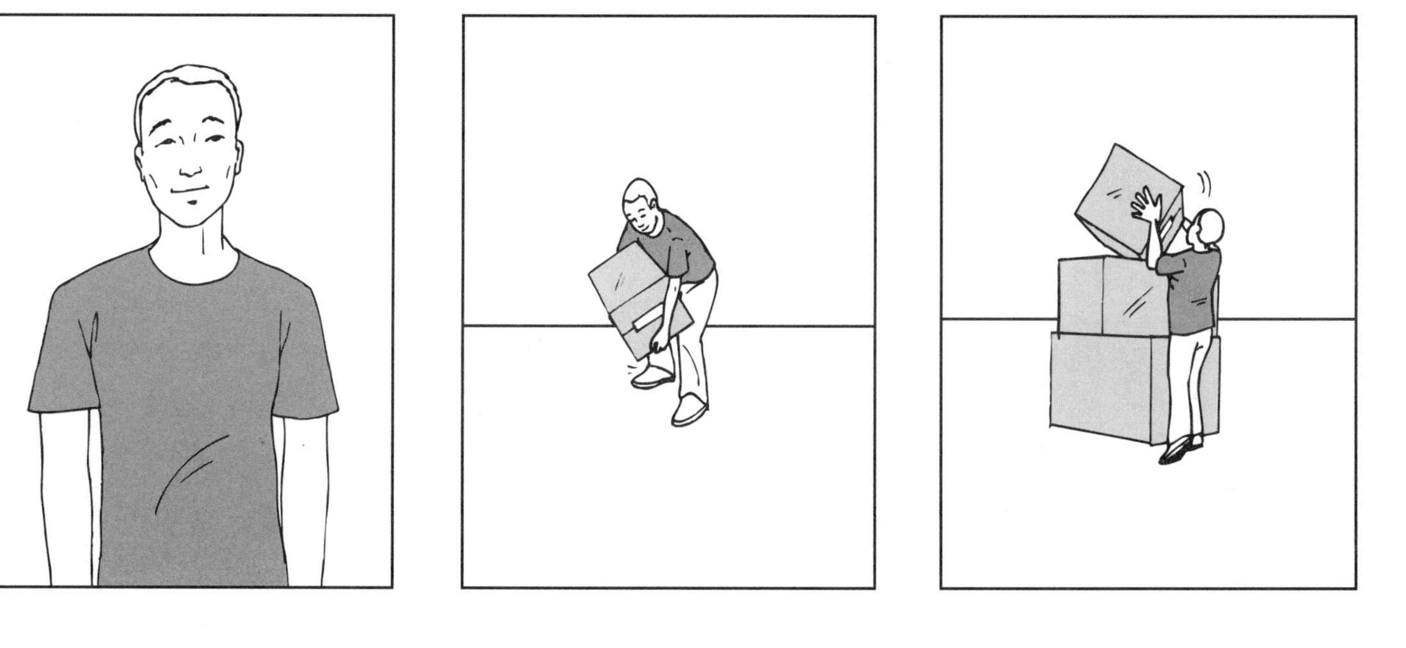

18

19

20

Noun + Verb + Adverb

1. The bus stopped slowly.
2. The girls talk quietly.
3. The girl dances gracefully.
4. The girl looks carefully.
5. The bell rings loudly.
6. The man runs fast.
7. The children dressed warmly.
8. The cheerleaders yell loudly.
9. The boy moved closer.
10. The clock ticks loudly.
11. The balloon rose higher.
12. The turtle walks slowly.
13. The children act friendly.
14. The lightning flashes brightly.
15. The men hold on tightly.
16. The star shines brightly.
17. The boy runs slowly.
18. The child prints neatly.
19. The woman yawns sleepily.
20. The boy pulls tightly.

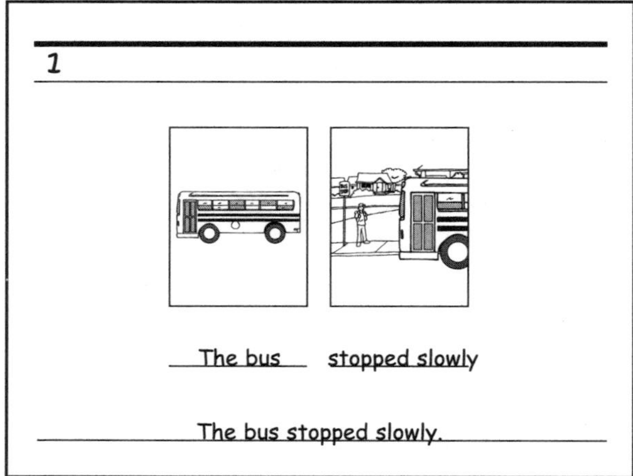

Modeling Example:

1. The first picture shows "**The bus**." Let's write that under the picture.
2. In the next picture, what has happened? The bus stopped. Let's add a word to tell how it stopped. We might say "**stopped slowly**." Let's write that down.
3. Now let's put the words all together to tell all about the last picture. "**The bus stopped slowly**."

1

2

3

4

5

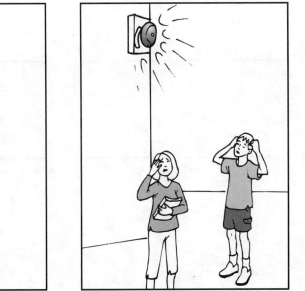

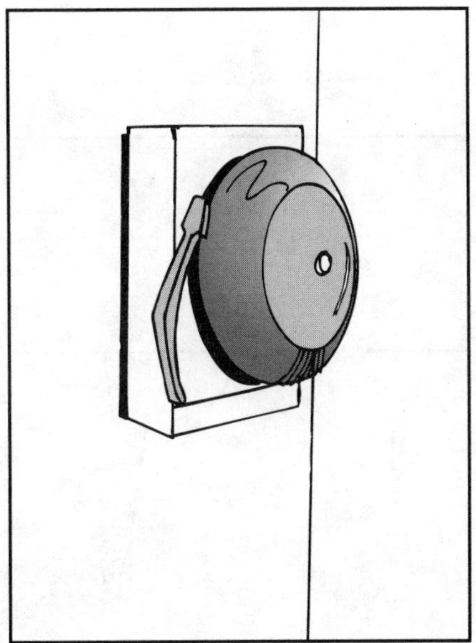

6

7

GO, TEAM!!

9

10

11

12

13

14

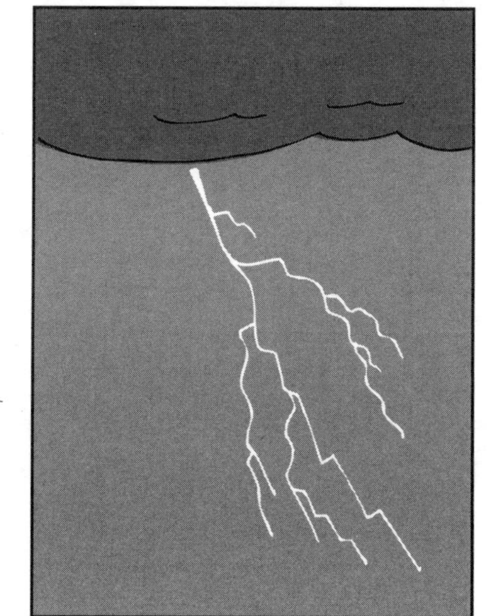

15

16

17

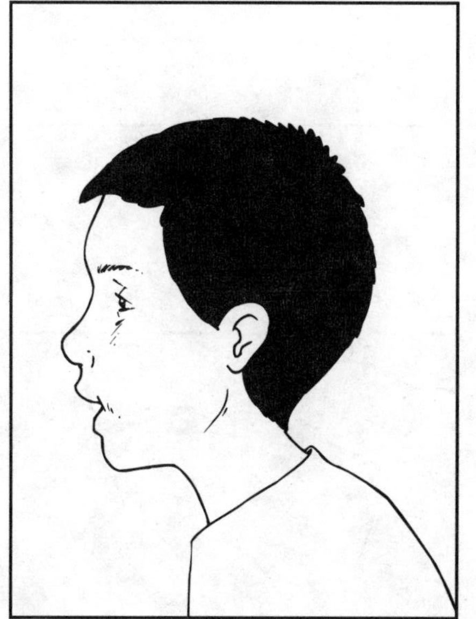

18

19

20

Noun + Verb + Direct Object + Indirect Object

1. The man is selling a car to the woman.
2. The father is peeling a banana for the child.
3. The father is holding a bottle for the baby.
4. The nurse is giving a shot to the boy.
5. The man is making a sandwich for the girl.
6. The boy is picking a flower for his mom.
7. The boy is throwing a Frisbee to the dog.
8. The man is giving a ticket to the girl.
9. The woman is taking a picture of the child.
10. The mother is handing the phone to her daughter.

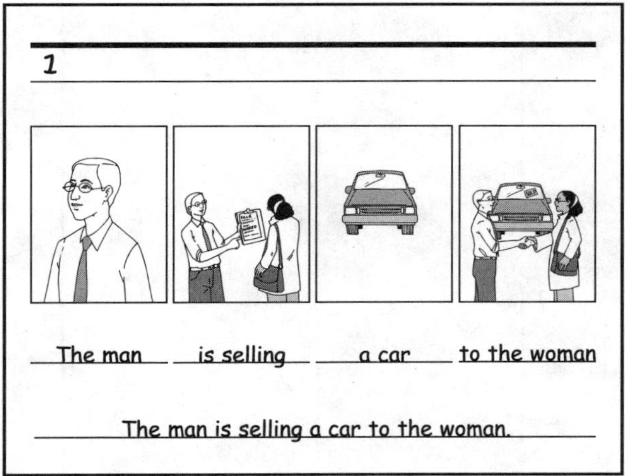

Modeling Example:

1. The first picture shows us "**The man**." Let's write that under the picture.
2. In the next picture, the man is doing something. What could he be doing? He is selling something. We might say "**is selling**." Let's write that down.
3. Look at the next picture. What do you see? "**A car**." Let's write that under that picture.
4. Look at the last picture. Who is the man selling the car to? "**The woman**." Let's write that under the picture.
5. Now let's put the words all together to tell everything that is happening in the last picture. "**The man is selling a car to the woman**."

1

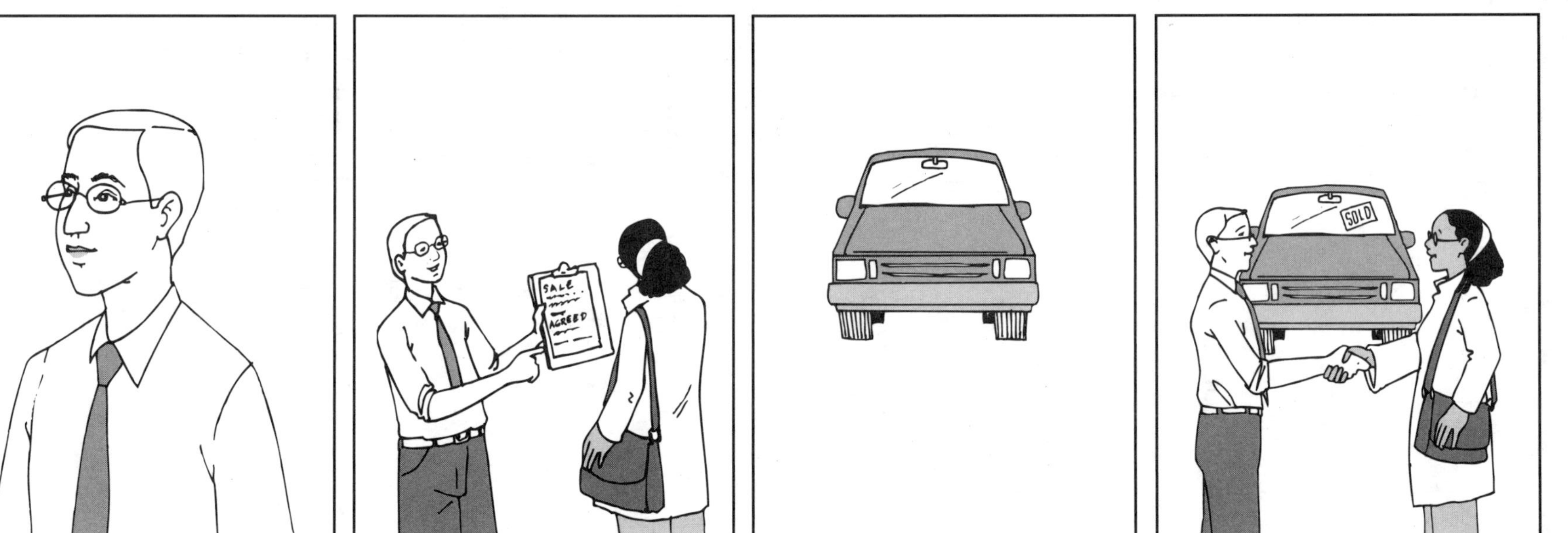

2

3

4

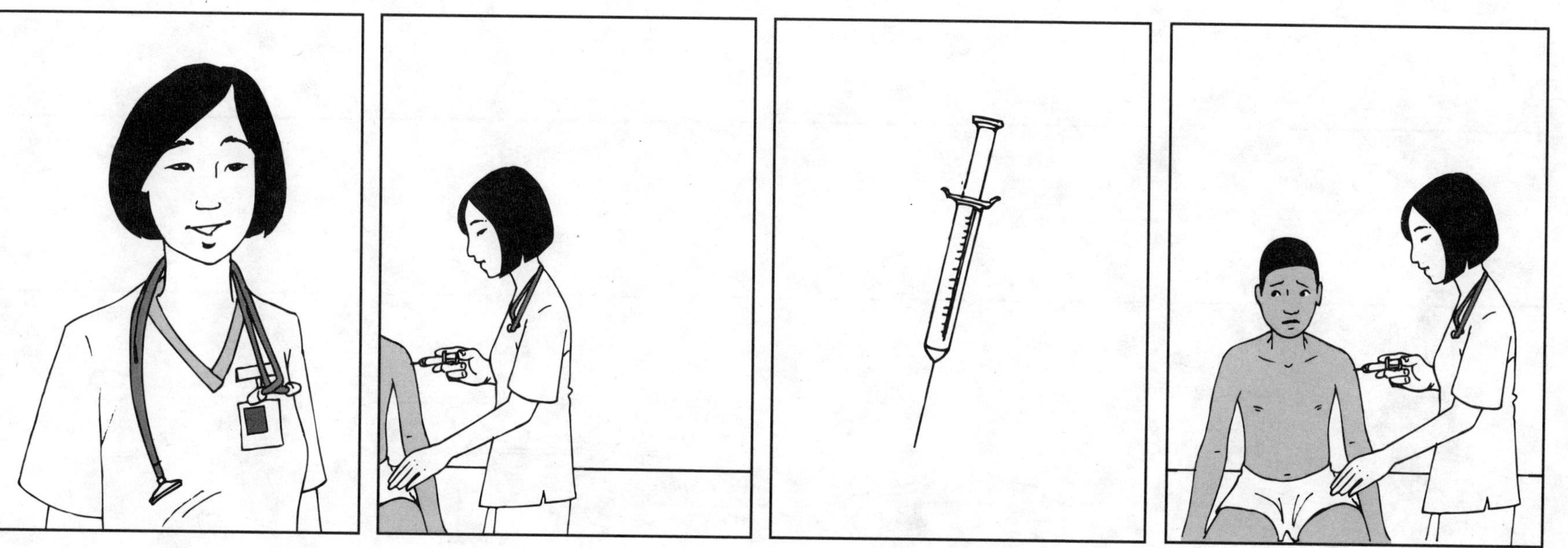

5

6

7

8

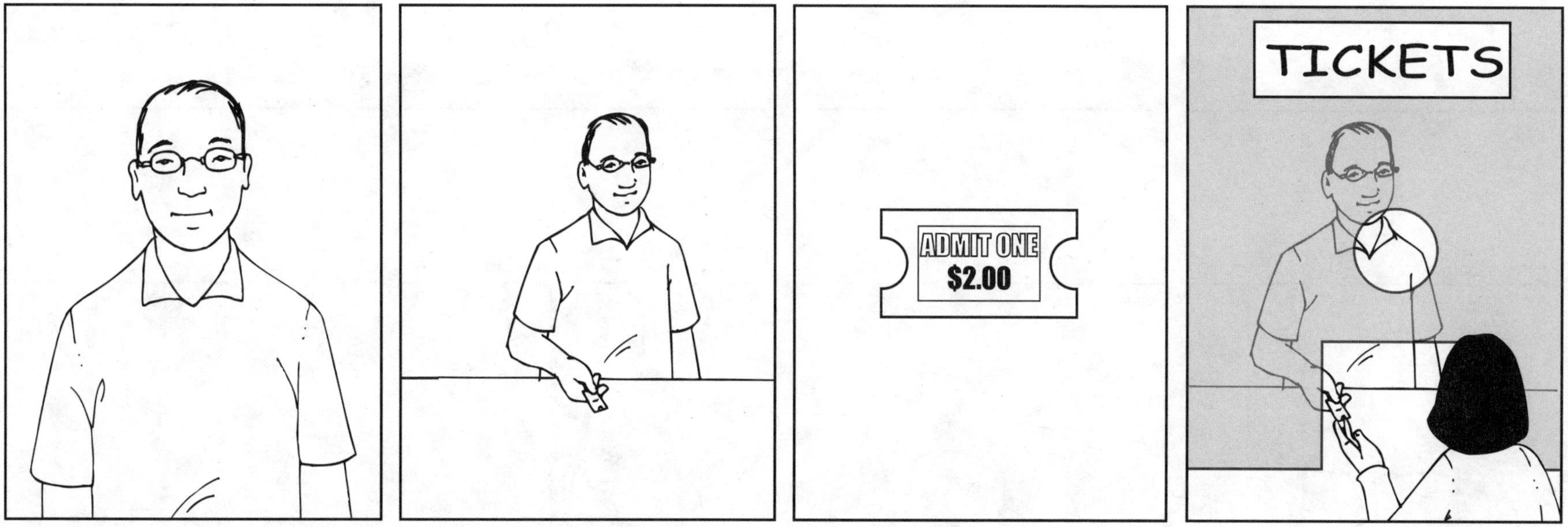

9

10

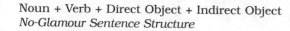

Noun + Prepositional Phrase + Verb

1. The boy in the bed is sleeping.
2. The children in the tent are sleeping.
3. The bear in the cave is sleeping.
4. The boy in the bathtub is singing.
5. The children in the choir are singing.
6. The bird in the nest is singing.
7. The girl at the table is eating.
8. The cats with stripes are eating.
9. The cow in the barn is eating.
10. The boy on the swing is smiling.
11. The boy on the ladder is painting.
12. The boy with the backpack is walking.
13. The boy with the hat is bouncing.
14. The girl with the doll is crying.
15. The girl on the slide is waving.
16. The girl behind the door is hiding.
17. The girl on the phone is talking.
18. The girl in the bathing suit is diving.
19. The children on the trampoline are jumping.
20. The boy in the car is reading.

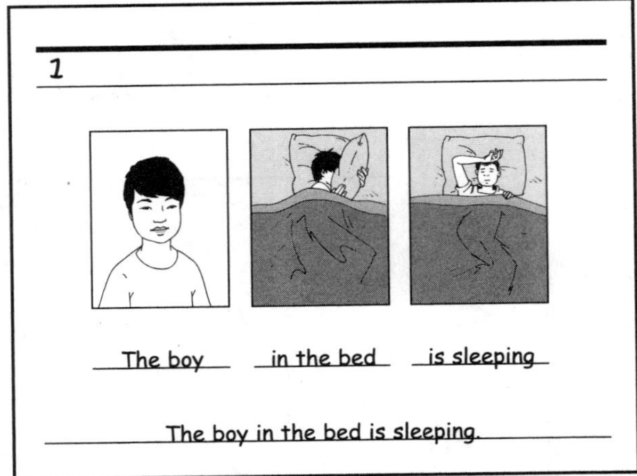

Modeling Example:

1. The first picture shows "**The boy**." Let's write that under the picture.
2. In the next picture, where is the boy? He's in the bed. Let's write "**in the bed**" under the picture.
3. Look at the next picture. What is the boy doing? He's sleeping. Let's write "**is sleeping**" under the picture.
4. Now let's put the words all together to tell all about the last picture. "**The boy in the bed is sleeping.**"

1

2

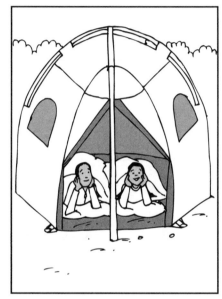

3

4

5

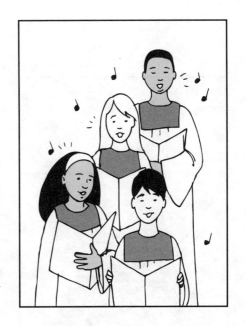

6

7

_______________ _______________ _______________

8

9

10

11

12

13

14

15

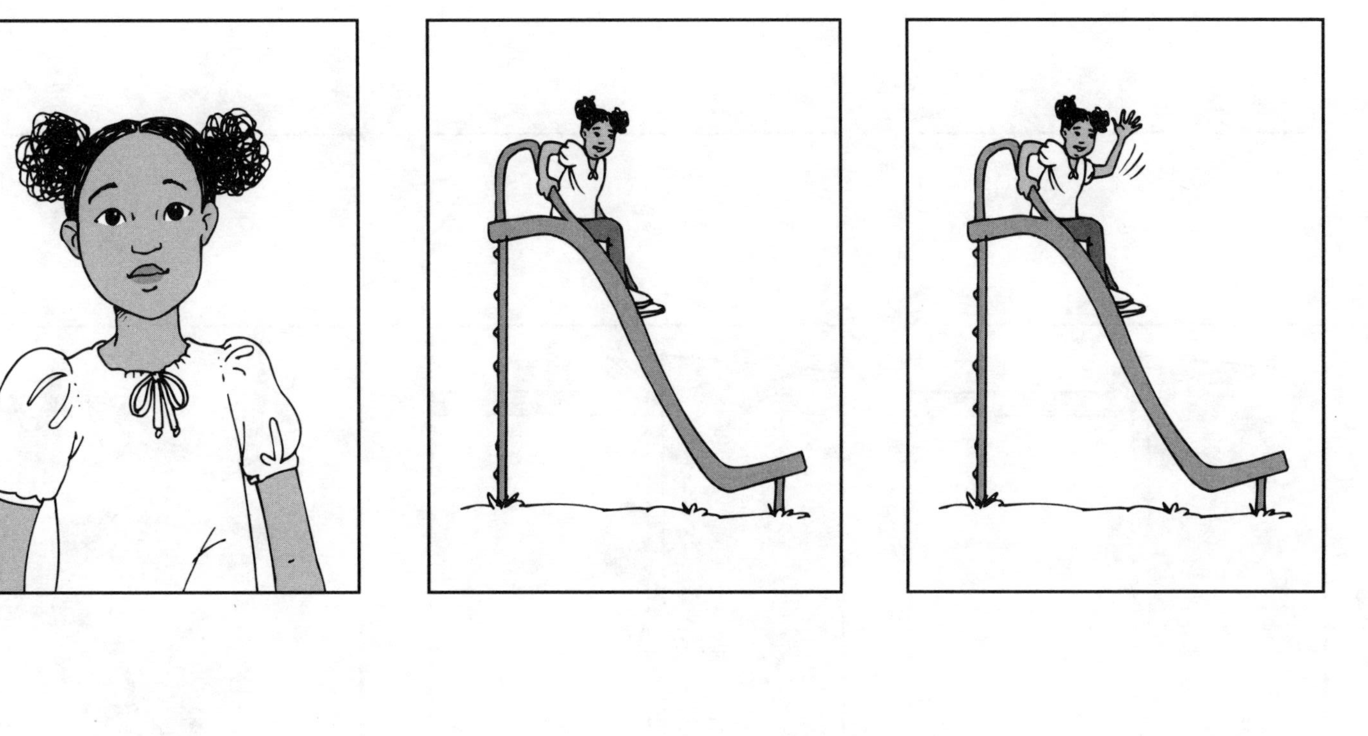

16

17

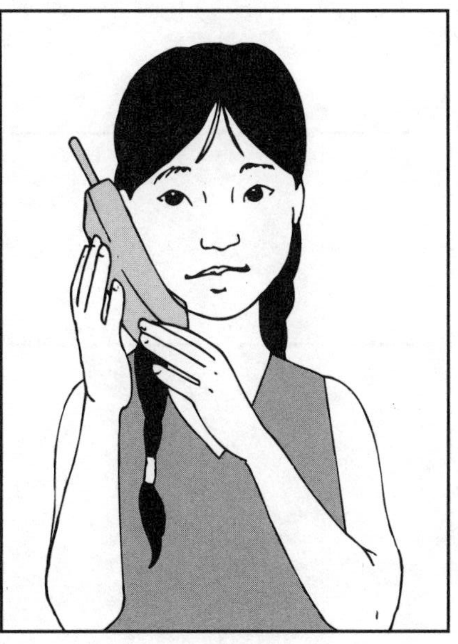

Noun + Prepositional Phrase + Verb
No-Glamour Sentence Structure

18

19

20

Noun + Verb + Adjective + Direct Object

1. The boy is watching the buzzing bee.
2. The woman is holding the crying baby.
3. The girl is answering the ringing phone.
4. The boy is painting a smiling face.
5. The woman is rocking the sleeping baby.
6. The boy is watching the sinking boat.
7. The boy is chasing the barking dog.
8. The girl is licking the melting ice cream.
9. The girl is watching the shining star.
10. The woman is hugging the crying child.

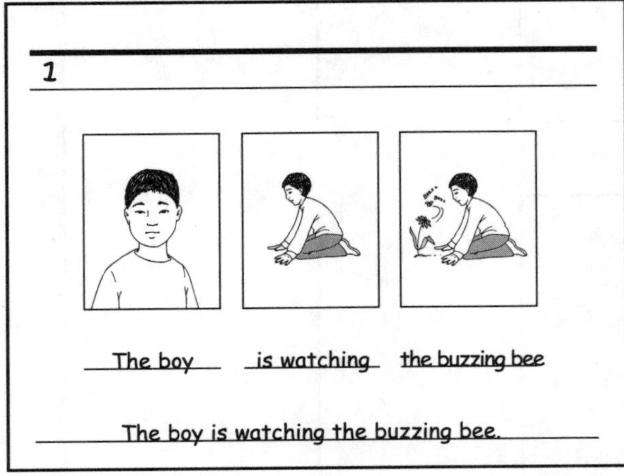

Modeling Example:

1. The first picture shows "**The boy**." Let's write that under the picture.
2. In the next picture, what has changed? The boy is watching something. We might say "**is watching**." Let's write that down.
3. Look at the next picture. What is the boy watching? "**The buzzing bee**." Let's write that down.
4. Now let's put the words all together to tell all about the last picture. "**The boy is watching the buzzing bee**."

1

2

3

4

5

6

7

8

9

10

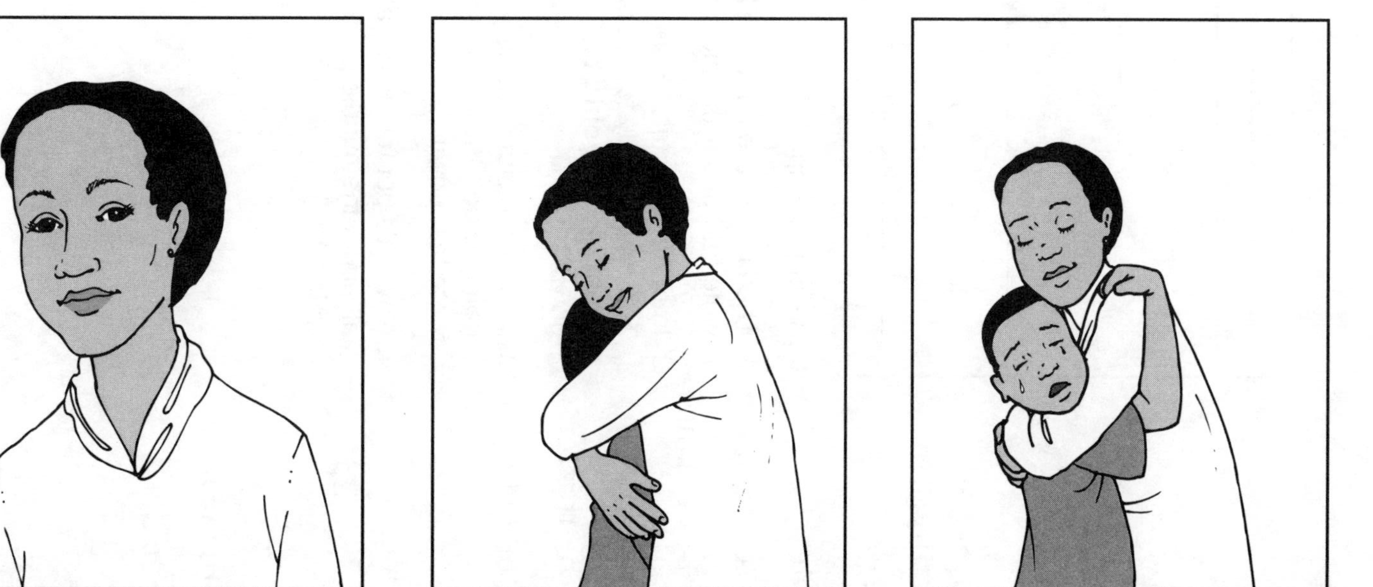

Noun + Verb + Infinitive/Infinitive Phrase

1. The boy is going to dive.
2. The boy is going to drink.
3. The boy is going to blow bubbles.
4. The boy is going to brush his teeth.
5. The boy is going to open the present.
6. The girl is going to run.
7. The girl is going to color a picture.
8. The girl is going to eat an apple.
9. The girl is going to win a trophy.
10. The girl is going to read a book.
11. The children are going to play basketball.
12. The children are going to swim.
13. The woman is going to drive the tractor.
14. The man is going to barbecue the hot dogs.
15. The man is going to climb the tree.
16. The man is going to tie his shoe.
17. The men are going to climb the mountain.
18. The bird is going to fly away.
19. The woman is going to wash the clothes.
20. The girl is going to brush her hair.

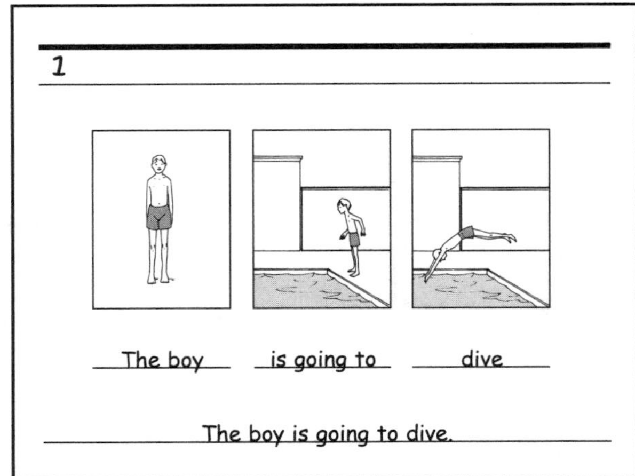

Modeling Example:

1. The first picture shows "**The boy**." Let's write that under the picture.
2. In the next picture, what has changed? The boy is ready to do something. We might say "**is going to**." Let's write that down.
3. The next picture shows what the boy is going to do. We might say "**dive**." Let's write that down.
4. Now let's put the words all together to tell all about the middle picture. "**The boy is going to dive**."

1

2

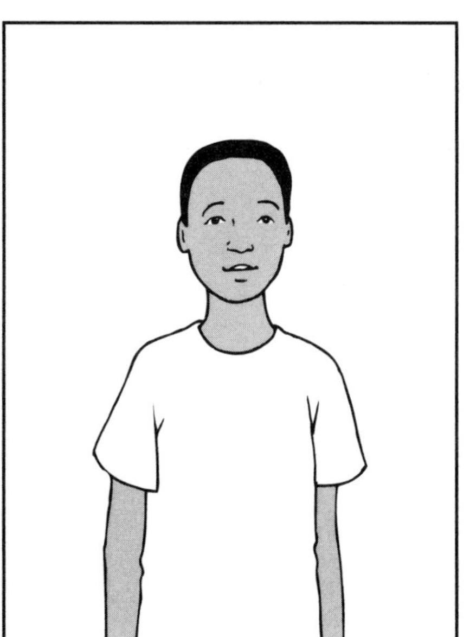

3

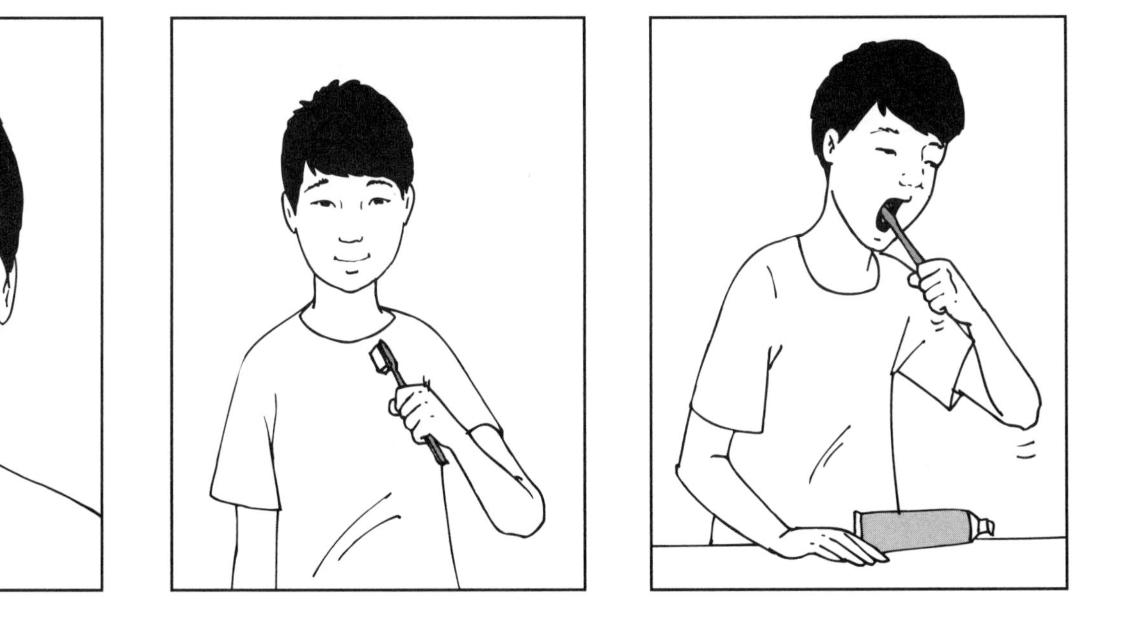

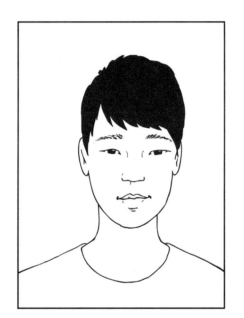

5

6

7

8

9

10

11

12

13

14

15

16

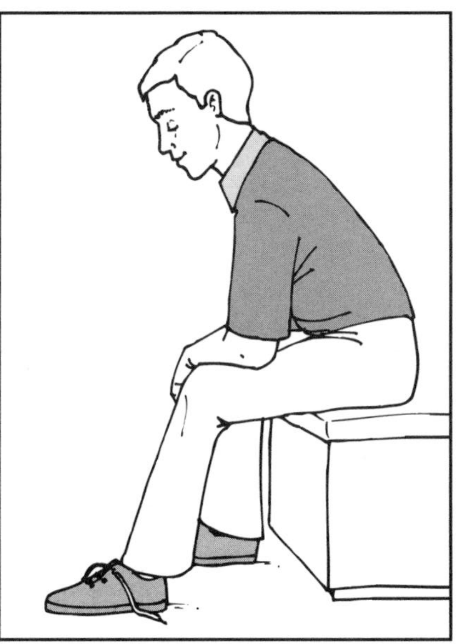

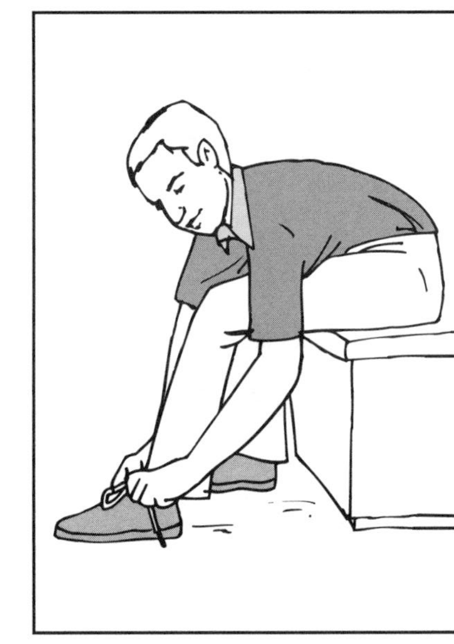

17

18

19

20

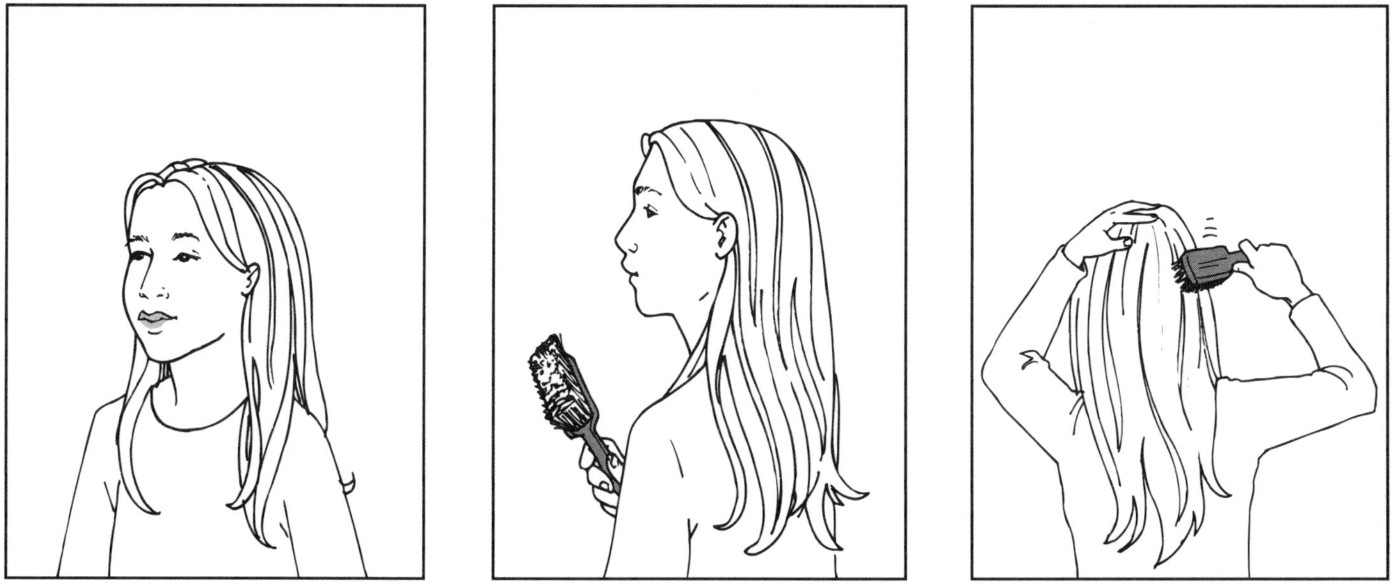

Noun + Adjective Clause + Verb/(Verb + Direct Object)

1. The girl who skinned her knee is crying.
2. The girl who is wearing a helmet is riding a bike.
3. The girl who hit the ball is running.
4. The woman who baked the cake won the prize.
5. The boy who is wearing a cap is blowing bubbles.
6. The boy who is wearing glasses is reading.
7. The boy who baked the cookies is sharing them.
8. The dog that is wearing a collar won the ribbon.
9. The boy who bought the pumpkin carved a face.
10. The cat that is climbing the tree is chasing a bird.

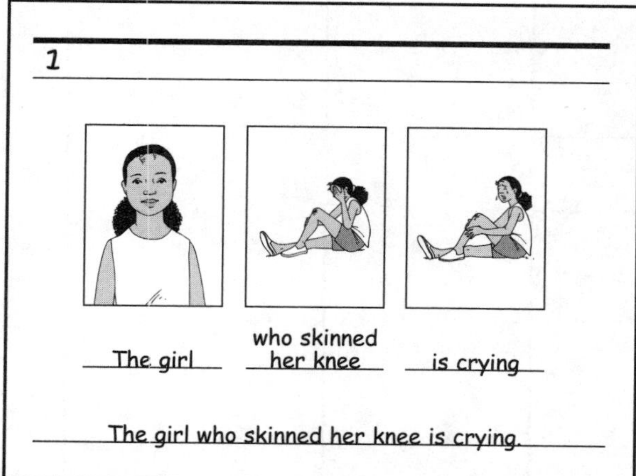

Modeling Example:

1. The first picture shows "**The girl**." Let's write that under the picture.
2. In the next picture, we see the girl again. She skinned her knee. She's not just any girl, she's the girl *who* skinned her knee. We might say "**who skinned her knee**." Let's write that down.
3. Now look at the last picture. What is the girl doing there? She's crying. Let's write "**is crying**" under the picture.
4. Now let's put the words all together to tell all about the last picture. "**The girl who skinned her knee is crying**."

1

2

3

4

5

6

_______________ _______________ _______________

7

8

9

10

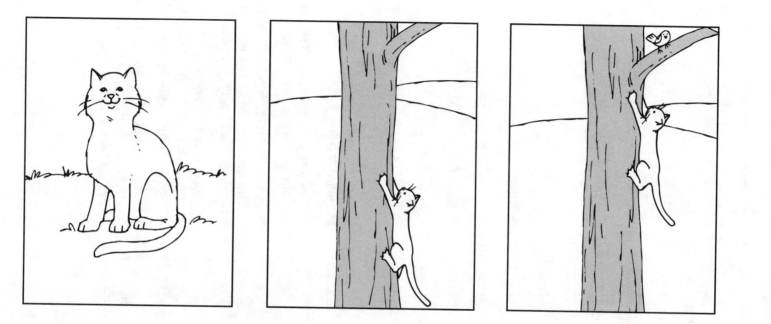

Noun + Verb + Adjective + Adverbial Clause

1. The girl is crying because she lost her balloon.
2. The girl is sad because her doll is broken.
3. The boy is scared because the dog is barking.
4. The woman is angry because her window is broken.
5. The man is hot because he is running.
6. The dog is wet because it is raining.
7. The cat is afraid because the dog is chasing it.
8. The team is excited because they won.
9. The fisherman was happy because he caught a big fish.
10. The boy was proud because he scored a goal.

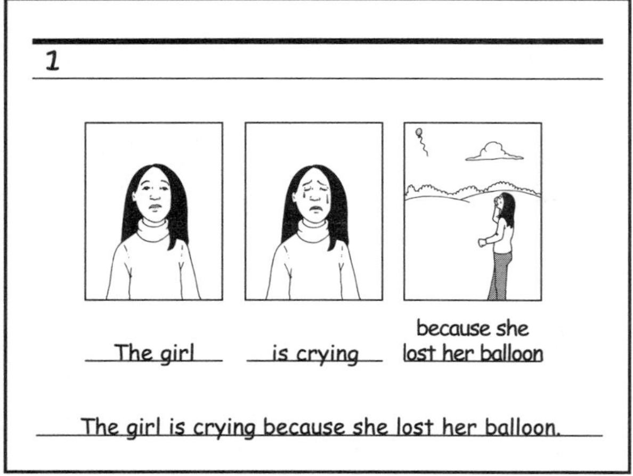

Modeling Example:

1. The first picture shows "**The girl**." Let's write that under the picture.
2. In the next picture, what is happening? The girl is crying. We might say "**is crying**." Let's write that down.
3. The last picture shows why the girl is crying. We might say "**because she lost her balloon**." Let's write that down.
4. Now let's put the words all together to tell all about the last picture. "**The girl is crying because she lost her balloon**."

1

2

3

4

5

Noun + Verb + Adjective + Adverbial Clause
No-Glamour Sentence Structure

6

7

10
6
11
71
12

10
11

6
STATE
CHAM

9

Noun + Negative Verb Phrase

1. The girl is not wearing a hat.
2. The girl is not sitting down.
3. The girl is not crying.
4. The girl is not drinking.
5. The girl is not sleeping.
6. The boy is not waving.
7. The boy is not reading.
8. The boy is not playing.
9. The boy is not running.
10. The boy is not watching.
11. The children are not smiling.
12. The children are not singing.
13. The children are not swimming.
14. The dog is not barking.
15. The cat is not scratching.
16. The cat is not washing.
17. The bird is not singing.
18. The duck is not swimming.
19. The cow is not eating.
20. The kangaroo is not hopping.

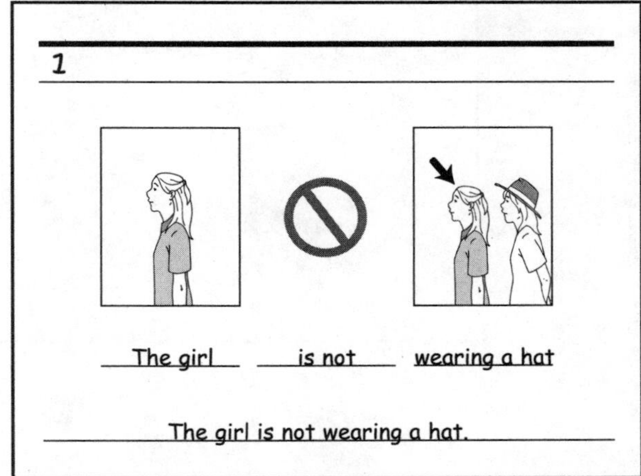

Modeling Example:

1. The first picture shows "**The girl**." Let's write that under the picture.
2. We're going to talk about what is *not* happening in this picture. Look at the symbol for **is not**. Let's write "**is not**" under the symbol.
3. Now look at the second picture. What is this girl (point to the girl with the hat) doing that the other girl is not doing? "**Wearing a hat**." Let's write that down.
4. Now let's put the words all together to tell all about the first picture. "**The girl is not wearing a hat**."

1

2

3

4

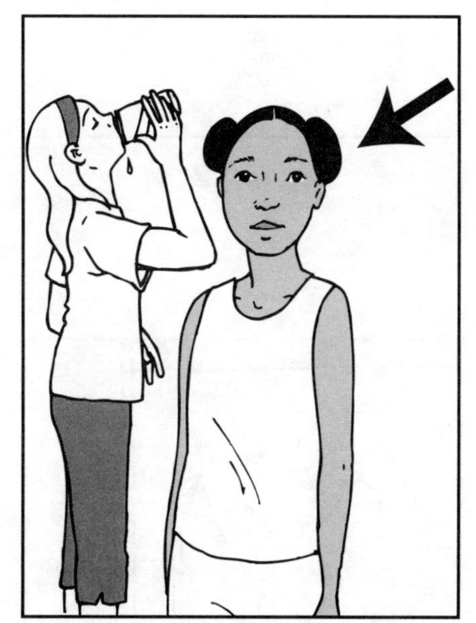

5

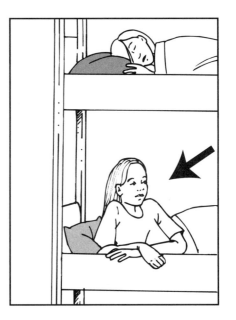

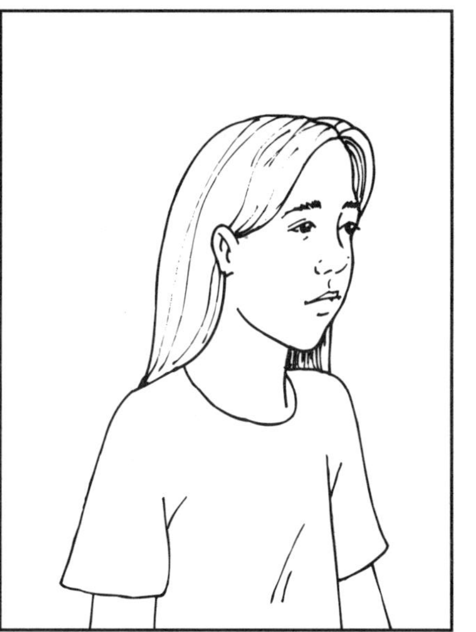

6

7

8

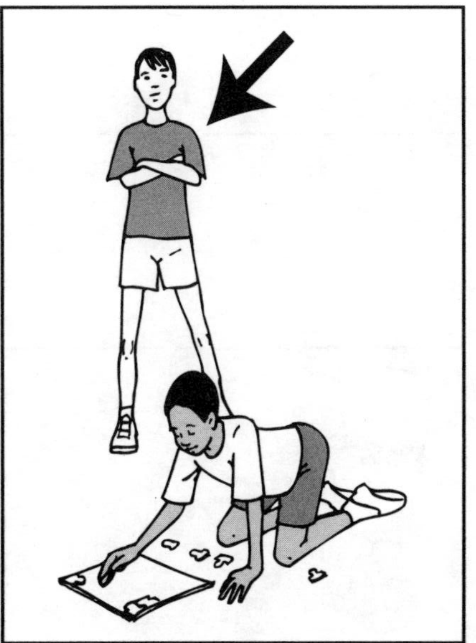

9

10

11

12

13

14

15

16

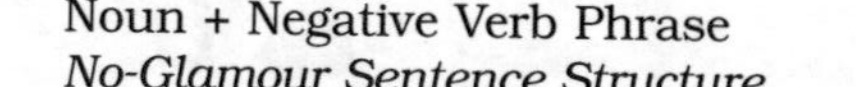

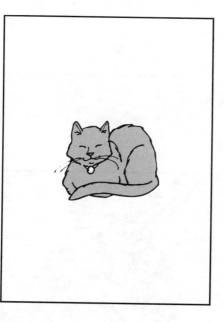

17

18

19

20

Word Cards

Copy this page on sturdy paper and then cut the words apart. Use them with students who need extra visual cueing.

the	a	an
is	are	was
were	her	his
by	to	for
in	on	with
at	going to	because
not	who	that

21-03-987654321

